THE SCIENCE LECTURE ROOM

SfB (97)
UDC 727.3

JEREMY TAYLOR M.A. A.R.I.B.A.

THE SCIENCE LECTURE ROOM

A planning study to examine the principles of location and design

of lecture rooms in the development of university science areas

Prepared with the support of the Nuffield Foundation

at the School of Architecture, Cambridge

CAMBRIDGE AT THE UNIVERSITY PRESS 1967

Published by the Syndics of the Cambridge University Press
Bentley House, 200 Euston Road, London, N.W. 1
American Branch: 32 East 57th Street, New York, N.Y. 10022

Library of Congress Catalogue Card Number: 67–24941

Printed in Great Britain
at the University Printing House, Cambridge
(Brooke Crutchley, University Printer)

CONTENTS

ACKNOWLEDGEMENTS

I would like to express my thanks to the Nuffield Foundation not only for financing this study but also for their support of my original proposals. And to Professor Sir Leslie Martin for all his encouragement and advice and for the facilities provided for me to work at the School of Architecture, Cambridge.

During the course of these studies I have had most valuable help from Messrs K. W. Monk and P. H. Dunstone, F./F.R.I.C.S., and I am grateful for the assistance of their computer section under Mr David Smart, and for the time he devoted to this project. I would also like to thank their associate Mr Michael Dwelly for his detailed help in the production of the cost analyses.

In my general collection of information and visits to survey university lecture rooms in England, I received much detailed assistance from the administrative, teaching and departmental staff concerned. Not only were they at all times extremely helpful but I was most impressed by their very real interest to obtain information on this subject, and in any guiding principles or methods of planning that might result.

Others whose various contributions and evidence I would particularly like to acknowledge here include Mr A. E. Watts of Messrs Edward A. Pearce and Partners, Consulting Engineers; Mr A. M. P. Brookes; Mr Peter Chamberlin; Mr Richard Sheppard; Sir Lawrence Bragg, F.R.S.; Mr Michael Clarke; Mr Peter Laslett and Mr A. Tattersall. I have also received information from the architects section of the University Grants Committee and the University Building Information Service.

For my analysis of science lecture rooms outside the U.K. I am indebted to Mr Peter Jockusch and Mr F. Stuer of the Staatshochbauamt fur die T.H. Dortmund for all their aid in arranging for me to visit and discuss recent university projects in Germany; to Professor Fritz Eller of the Institut fur Schulbau, Aaachen; the office of architects Messrs Hentrich, Petschnigg and Partners, Bochum; Professor Horst Linde Finanz ministerium, Baden Wurttemberg. In Holland my thanks are due to Mr Ooms of T.H. Delft and Mr A. J. Rieken of N.V. Bureau Voor het Samenstellen van Bouw-programmas. From the U.S.A. Mr F. G. Matsler of the Co-ordinating Council for Higher Education, San Francisco has made available the results of their considerable research into university laboratory and classroom facilities.

INTRODUCTION

This study, aimed at suggesting methods and principles of planning for the lecture room within a university science area, has also had to perform a separate task in collecting together factual data on existing lecture rooms. Up to this time no documentation or central source could provide information on such questions as: where are the science lecture rooms in a typical U.K. university, what size are they, how are they distributed by subjects, how are they designed and perhaps most important what use are they put to. In addition, published information on this type of teaching space has been extremely limited and confined more to illustrating architectural form than to a serious examination of planning principles. To supplement the basic framework of facts obtained by survey a review has also been made of statements on the future pattern of science teaching and the likely role of the lecture within it.

What has emerged clearly is evidence of the wastage that results from the arbitrary sizes and designs of lecture rooms embedded in science buildings and built solely to meet the needs of specialised departments. Not only do existing rooms show a record of low utilisation compounded with low occupancy but, in addition, their physical location renders them unsuitable for higher efficiency through central control and shared use. As an alternative to this situation lecture rooms have been considered not as individual and separate spaces but as groupings of rooms within an overall science development and directly related to the supporting teaching areas. From this it has been possible to put forward principles for the location and size of such groupings to meet the requirements of any particular teaching load and minimum standards of plant use.

A series of models for lecture-room groupings was made in order to compare the building needs for a given situation to those at differing levels of room utilisation. To give a physical form to these and to allow for a rationalisation of design and space standards, a mathematical program was set up for the delineation by computer of acceptable lecture-room conditions. This allowed for room forms to be selected to satisfy varying presentation criteria and to provide these on an equal basis for comparison. The program has also been used to demonstrate a method of flexibility for changes in the room sizes of a typical lecture grouping and so to allow for any future alterations in the teaching pattern.

Due to the lack of any significant information on the cost of lecture rooms in the U.K. it was necessary to establish a theoretical basis for the cost studies. These examine the difference between groupings of lecture rooms required to meet the needs of a given science area and an equivalent series of single lecture rooms embedded in departmental buildings. Not only were these studies able to show major economics by considering the overall development, not just individual building units, but they were also able to equate higher standards of utilisation with potential savings in capital cost.

The extent of the study has been focused on one lecture-room type, for the Natural Sciences, so that the subject can be examined in detail and methods of approach for future planning suggested. From this it is then a direct step to parallel the work for other lecture-room types, e.g. Arts or Technology, or even amend it to suit the investigation of different categories of university space; in this way a further build-up of data on the lecture room could be made possible and a process of testing out these initial findings established.

The detailed investigation of environmental aspects of design, e.g. heating or ventilation, have not been included as they represent criteria which support the principles and methods proposed but which are not central to them. In addition, there is a general absence of agreement on standards and levels of use in these fields which is now being recognised and is encouraging considerable new research work, such as that recently reported on the problems of ventilation system noise.

Following on from the scope of this planning study there are apparent many areas where further basic survey and development work could usefully be continued:

1   The collection of simple, factual information on the location, floor space and use of existing university facilities in the U.K. This will need to be by a central organisation who can ensure that such information is readily accessible and obtained to a uniform basis.

2   An inquiry into levels of occupancy of lecture rooms and achievable utilisation for shared use should be made by universities and tested out against proposed minimum standards. This could be combined with development work on the use of computer controlled timetabling in relation to the total lecture needs of a university.

3   Space standards for lecture-room groupings and in particular for their ancillary, e.g. foyer, areas require to be developed to act as a guide to universities and their architects.

4   The cost studies for lecture-room groupings should be enlarged to provide information on complex designs of more than one level of rooms. Cost data on new lecture rooms built or planned needs to be compiled in a form suitable for comparative and elemental analysis.

5   More detailed studies for flexibility and adaptability in the planning of lecture groupings could also examine the likely economies of a preferred range of basic lecture-room sizes designed to make use of a system of standardised building elements.

6   An investigation into the design of teaching stations or complete lecture units which could form part of the standard equipment of science laboratory areas. They represent a different category of lecture facility from the common user groupings proposed and could be produced as prefabricated or 'packaged' elements to a standard dimensional specification.

7   The development of a satisfactory means of presenting the television image as a visual aid in the ordinary lecture room. This needs to overcome the present drawbacks of small monitor sets placed around the room or the expensive and space consuming back and rear projection systems. The most promising line of research here appears to be the possibility of electro-luminescent television screens which could be hung on the wall and made to any required image size.

Items such as these require, however, to be part of a co-ordinated research programme which can be centrally controlled and sponsored and constantly developed with time and experience. At present the only organisation suitable for this role remains the U.G.C. So far though they have had to act primarily as a rationing organisation with their available staff deployed to check detailed designs submitted to them by universities and their architects. What is needed beyond this is now a real background of factual information and research to act as guidance in the establishing of principles of university planning and as a rational basis of grant apportionment.

1 Scroope Terrace, Cambridge   JEREMY TAYLOR
May 1966

I
CONTEXT OF THE SCIENCE LECTURE ROOM

1. THE ACADEMIC CONTEXT

a. Existing Teaching Patterns

As a basis for the investigation of planning and design principles for the science lecture room it is necessary first to outline the present structure of university science teaching and to consider the direction of its future development. This then allows architectural decisions to be analysed as a reflection of established academic policies and also in relation to new or emergent teaching patterns requiring revised building forms.

The role of the lecture within the existing academic structure is indicated by the following table showing average hours of teaching received per week by full-time undergraduates in British universities during spring 1961–62:[1]

	Lectures*	Discussion	Practicals	Other	All teaching
All U/G	8·1	2·0	4·8	0·5	15·9
Humanities	6·8	2·3	0·6	0·4	10·1
Science	8·3	1·0	7·8	0·3	17·4
Applied Science	10·8	0·9	6·9	1·3	19·9

* Definitions given by the Committee on University Teaching Methods (ch. Hale):

Lecture means a teaching period occupied wholly or mainly with continuous exposition by the lecturer. Students attending it may be given some opportunity for questions or a little discussion, but in the main they have nothing to do but listen and take notes.

Discussion period. This differs from a lecture in requiring much more participation from the student. For example, there may be reading and study of a paper by a student; discussion, in which students are meant to take part, of topics introduced by a member of staff or a student.

In giving these figures the Committee on Higher Education commented:[2] 'We think that a well-planned and well-delivered series of lectures can give a sense of proportion and emphasis lacking in tutorial discussions and seminars where teaching, in following where the argument leads, may often stray into byways. It should bring to students modifications of what they find in their textbooks, suggest wider reading, and, when given by lecturers in touch with recent developments, be a source of stimulus and inspiration. We are particularly thinking here of lectures to large audiences in which a genuinely synoptic view of a subject is given. Lectures of this kind which lay down principles and survey a subject widely are particularly valuable for first-year students. Attendance at lectures gives them a necessary frame to a week's work, makes them feel a part of a community of learning, and leads them to a wider intellectual contact with their fellows than membership of small classes can give.'

A further interpretation of the traditional role of the lecture was given by the Committee on Teaching Methods:[3] 'In science especially lectures are considered to be the best way to present material which would be too complex to understand without oral explanation or too wasteful of time to acquire otherwise. . . . Moreover, in science, and also in mathematics, lectures have the advantage over books that by the use of visual aids complex diagrams and formulae can be built up gradually and structures with more than two dimensions can be displayed.'

1. Bibl. 3, p. 185.   2. Bibl. 3, p. 187.   3. Bibl. 5, p. 53.

The size of classes in U.K. universities for spring 1961/62 was also given by the Committee on Higher Education and showed that attendance, by average numbers, of undergraduates for all types of Science teaching period was:[1]

Lectures	Discussion	Practical	All
31·0	3·6	18·3	18·2

The size of undergraduate lectures broken down by categories of audience size was:[2]

	No of students present				
	1–4 %	5–9 %	10–19 %	20–100 %	over 100 %
Pure Science	6	14	22	49	8
Humanities	18	20	25	36	4
Year 1	5	8	17	61	9
Other non-final	11	16	26	44	3
Final year (specialists)	18	27	31	23	1
All students	12	18	25	41	4

Apart from indicating the trend to have larger lectures for the Sciences than for the Humanities (Science median size: 33 as opposed Humanities: 15) and the general falling off of lecture sizes after Year 1, the most startling implication of these figures was that over half of all the university lectures in U.K. were given to less than 20 people. As the Vice-Chancellor of Essex pointed out: 'We cannot afford the inefficiency of such preparation and delivery'.[3]

The Committee themselves recommended that lectures should normally be devoted to the exposition of principles to large audiences and that there was 'little virtue in formal lectures to very small audiences'.[4]

A rather similar point was discussed by the Californian 'Restudy' of 1955: 'Class size is also related to teaching method. Some courses may be conducted just as well in large lecture classes as in small discussion groups, or in a combination of lecture and discussion sections. If the principal purpose of the course is to present information (not a very desirable objective of classroom teaching) large sections may be as satisfactory as small ones. On the other hand, if discussion and analysis are necessary to attain the goals of the course, relatively small sections are necessary. Judgements concerning satisfactory class size depend on the nature of the course, the outcomes desired and the teaching methods *actually* used. Small classes have been justified in some instances on the basis of need for class discussion and then taught by the lecture method.'[5]

In practice any planning decisions on the size of science lecture rooms will have to recognise the following academic determinants:

1   The teaching pattern for the sciences
2   Size of years, streams and practical classes
3   The role of the lecture room within this pattern
4   Maximum size of lecture for acceptable teaching presentation

The table shown earlier indicated that the average science undergraduate spent a nearly equal proportion of time on practical work and lectures. How this applies to Physics was described in more detail by R. G. Chambers in the *Bulletin of the Institute of*

1. Bibl. 3, Appendix 2(B), p. 335.   2. Bibl. 5, pp. 54, 55.   3. Bibl. 6, p. 48.
4. Bibl. 3, p. 187.   5. Bibl. 56, p. 450.

Physics,[1] A survey which he made of forty-seven departments in the U.K. showed that the 'average student' during three years spends:

8·5 hours per week in the laboratory
6·8 hours per week at lectures

and in analysing the usefulness of the practical (i.e. laboratory) classes Chambers commented: 'The central fact surely is that lectures and laboratory work are no longer complementary methods of teaching the same subject as they were perhaps sixty years ago. In 1900, to exaggerate a little, the lecturer told the student all about the different ways . . . and the student then went away and applied all these methods in the practical class; the chief function of laboratory work was to illustrate and drive home points from lectures as it still is in schools today.'

Part of a general survey of science lecture rooms carried out in the University of Cambridge in 1964 showed the following requirements by departments:

Subject	Lecture related to laboratory work	Lecture demonstrates principle only
Chemistry	—	*
Phys. Chem.	—	*
Botany	*	—
Geology	*	—
Biochemistry	—	*
Physics	—	*
Zoology	—	*

The same survey also showed how the size of the Cambridge science lectures given in 1964 was related to the structure of Part I (first years) and Part II (final year) teaching, e.g.:

Subject	Approx. size of lectures 1964		Comment by departments
	Part I	Part II	
Phys. Chem.	170 and 190	110	Part I classes to increase
Geology	80 to 100 year 1 40 to 60 year 2	10 to 15	—
Biochemistry	400	40 to 50	Part I to fall to 200 + with provision of Medical Sciences Tripos
Physics	320 to 360	150	Student pressures for future would require up to 800 + at Part I
Zoology	85 to 90 year 1 85 to 90 year 2	50 max.	Part II sizes limited by available departmental space

Departments such as Physics facing the prospect of a rapid expansion plan to break their Part I classes into several 'streams' of 200[2] dependent on ability or, as with Zoology, upon difference of emphasis in teaching.

The majority of Part I lectures bring together the students on a course from the smaller groups into which they are split for laboratory work. The ability of any department to accommodate a number of these laboratory class increments will therefore generate their overall requirements for lecture room capacity together with any related service teaching load. The size of these laboratory increments will depend on teaching pattern

1. Bibl. 12, p. 79.
2. Considered by many teachers interviewed here to be the maximum viable size for traditional lecturing.

and capacity of teaching spaces. Chambers in his analysis of Physics classes[1] showed that average size using the laboratory at any one time was:

Year	1	42·1 students
	2	28·3 students
	3N	21·5 students

Part II lectures are to a much greater degree involved with advanced projects and research work and the pattern of lectures generally will be for smaller groups and need a greater flexibility than at the Part I stage. In particular departments commented that Part II lecture rooms are useful close to the laboratories so that students can adjourn to them for 'chance' or non-timetabled lectures whenever a problem needs discussion or a symposium is arranged. (No clear distinction was drawn between the existing situation and that which would be possible if in addition to lecture rooms for formal lectures special provision within the laboratory areas was made for these chance discussions.)

The examples for the University of Cambridge (pop. 9,170) represented the upper limits for science teaching loads found under the existing organisation of U.K. Universities. By contrast a small university will, over-all, have smaller teaching groups, e.g. University of Hull (pop. 2,243):

Zoology Department	Special Course	—16 a year (1964)
	Joint Course	—30 a year

These two courses do not meet but Year 1 and Year 2 are allowed to run together to give lecture sizes of 32 and 60.

Chemistry Department	Special Course	—70 a year (1964)
	Ancillary Course	—50 a year
	Joint Course	—12 a year

In this case there was no combining of classes or years.

What these courses at Hull and Cambridge both illustrate is the academic framework which has been general in the U.K. and has traditionally provided for university subjects to be studied in depth after specialisation at a school sixth form. In this it has been the exception in world higher education and not the rule.[2]

In Western Europe, for instance, where successful completion of the final school year gives automatic entry to higher education, there is often a very high rate of 'student wastage' through examination failure and it is common to spend as long as seven years on a nominal four-year course. A direct result of this can be the great strain put on building space and facilities and the uncertainty as to likely numbers; especially when examinations may be taken several times and lectures are open to all who register for them. The most popular courses may therefore require regular lectures for 500 to 600 students and capacities over 1,000 are not uncommon (see analysis of German lecture sizes, Chapter 4, Section *b*).

Although the lecture has been established throughout Europe as a primary teaching method since the first recognisable universities or 'studia generale' of the Middle Ages, the science lecture (as opposed to that for medicine) is a recent emergence as part of the university curriculum and did not become a serious competitor of the arts until the industrial revolution of the nineteenth century. While the Natural Sciences, together with Engineering, had first begun to be taught in separate universities on the Continent such as the École Polytechnique in Paris (1794) or the Technische Hochschule Vienna (1815), in England the comparative rate of growth was exceptionally slow, and at

1. Bibl. 12, p. 80.   2. Bibl. 3, p. 41.

Oxford and Cambridge slowest.[1] In fact, Cambridge did not seriously start building for the sciences until after 1860 and the Cavendish laboratory was not founded there until 1874. The initial emphasis of science lectures was on the complex demonstration, often given by the Professor in charge of the department, needing considerable apparatus and time for preparation. Experiments to show the discovery of a particular law or set of principles were common and represented the early application of teaching aids in the sciences.

During the twentieth century, the whole pattern of science teaching has been changed, not only by the opportunity to use a wide variety of visual aids, e.g. slides or film, but also by the immense range of subject-matter and published information which must now be included in any course. In particular the move away from long, highly organised demonstrations of principles is apparent in all science subjects although possibly least in Physics. Most departments and lecturers questioned felt that this was inevitable due to the rapid expansion of student numbers and also because, in the time available, the range of theoretical work to be covered did not allow the comparative luxury of setting up many experiments. The corollary to this is a greater reliance now placed on students doing complex practical work themselves in the laboratories and having the theory and technique explained to them there (it is noticeable that for the sciences it is in the laboratory that television as an aid to teaching is already most commonly in use). In addition the rapid development of 'periphery' subjects and the overlap of disciplines, for instance the need for Physics teaching in Zoology,[2] has meant that the subject-matter is becoming increasingly mathematical and theoretical and, as already referred to, the separation between lecture and laboratory work more distinct.

The exceptions to this decline in science lecture demonstrations are mainly where apparatus is used in the lecture to explain a conceptual difficulty, i.e. to demonstrate a phenomenon and not, as in the nineteenth century, take a class right through an experiment. (Although here again the ease with which films are obtained or slides made means that a rapid way of illustrating most problems can now be made available.) Also a number of departments readily accept that having demonstration lectures in the programme serves to ease the pace of teaching.

The way in which academic staff saw their likely requirements for presenting the various science subjects was indicated by a survey of Cambridge departments:

	Chem.	Phys. Chem.	Physics	Biochem.	Bot.	Zool.	Geol.
Complex demonstration	—	*	*	—	—	—	—
Models	*	—	*	—	—	*	—
Chalkboards	*	*	*	*	*	*	*
35 mm slides	*	*	*	*	*	*	*
Cine film	*	—	*	*	*	*	—
Epidiascope	—	—	—	—	*	—	—
Television (future)	—	—	*	—	—	*	—
Charts	*	—	—	—	*	*	*

* Teaching aids required.

Although this reflected individual preferences in one university it nevertheless confirmed certain general themes:

The central use of slides, screen wall images and chalkboard as teaching aids.
Science lecture rooms can be designed in general terms rather than individually for special subjects.

1. Bibl. 37, p. 239, where Dr N. Pevsner discusses the evolution of the university and its building requirements.
2. See, for instance, Professor Pringle's inaugural lecture on *The Two Biologies*, Bibl. 8.

How the student reacts to the existing methods of science lecture presentation has been considered by P. Marris in *The Experience of Higher Education*. Criticism was particularly heavy for the unintelligent use of the chalkboard in the sciences and the need for students often to spend most of their time copying notes or immaculate complex colour diagrams. What science students most wanted was that the lecturer should have an interest in the subject and be able to give his own point of view and use illustrations from his immediate experience (which perhaps suggests a specific case for lecture demonstrations on the grounds of gaining enthusiasm and technical interest). Marris commented:[1] 'I think that the essential function of a lecturer is to place knowledge in a meaningful context. . . . But, perhaps even more usefully, he can provide a more personal context showing why the subject interests and excites him and how he has used it in his own experience.'

And also:[2] 'The lecturer should act as a guide to the students' independent study providing a synthesis of the main points in the textbooks and references to further reading, especially in the latest work published in the journals.'

To satisfy any of these points however a lecturer has to have some sense of communication with his audience and this is necessarily related to the size of that audience. The question as to what are the acceptable limits for science lecture capacities in this context was one which produced the most varied evidence from lecturers of all universities. Many lecturers consider that ideally a class size of approximately 250 is the absolute maximum they can hope to communicate with, while 100 to 150 must be the maximum if practical demonstrations are carried out and to be of real value.[3] There was also support for the feeling that there is a fast falling off of teaching effectiveness once classes are much over 100.

The possible alternatives of lecture room size for new or redeveloped science areas are therefore:

Maximum to hold largest numbers of students to be lectured to at one time.

Room capacities broken down to correspond to chosen group, stream or year sizes.

Limit of room size decided by maximum that is thought acceptable for lecturing,[4] e.g. 200 to 250 (although some lecturers were in fact satisfied to lecture to 300 to 400).

Limit of room size chosen to give optimum communication lecturer to students, e.g. 100 or less.

In some cases, e.g. if maximum lecture numbers = course size and this were 100 or less, then there would be no initial conflict, although ideally first decisions on lecture room size should be seen as part of a policy which can then be maintained in the face of future university and subject expansion. Alternatively an arbitrary decision on size limits, e.g. no room larger than 160 for science lectures, will provide for good presentation conditions but may also inevitably mean that large course and year structures require greater staff: student numbers and extra built floor space per place. In neither of these cases though can there be an absolute answer; only increments of lecture room size will be fixed, based on an academic policy, and lecture buildings will need to provide the flexibility for additional increments to be added or the existing sizes rearranged.

1. Bibl. 7, p. 53.   2. Ibid. p. 48.

3. Definite criteria are of course available for calculating dimensions, e.g. maximum chalkboard to rear seat or minimum size of demonstration apparatus (see Chapter 6, Section *a*). For large audiences these requirements for seeing can be met by varying the presentation method as with larger overhead writing machines or the use of oversize demonstration models. A notable example of this perfecting of demonstrations for large audiences has been at the Royal Institution, London, where public science lectures are regularly given to 500 to 600.

4. As opposed to merely presenting information by audio visual means, e.g. by film or television where audience sizes are not relevant.

b. New Teaching Methods

Decisions on the size of science lecture rooms for the new universities in the U.K. show a distinct contrast with the patterns of size in the science areas of the older established universities. For example plans at 1965 gave:[1]

University of York: (phase 1 population 3,000)	first-stage science buildings to have 4 at 40-seat tiered theatres each of generous size so that 'up to 80 people can be accommodated in a nominal 40-place room'.[2]
Brunel University: (phase 1 population 4,000)	lecture block: 3 at 180, 3 at 100, 8 at 70 all tiered.
University of Essex: (phase 1 population 3,000)	originally planned to have 5 at 60 in new science block. This later amended to 3 at 60 and 1 at 150.
University of Surrey: (phase 1 population 3,000)	apart from a multi-purpose 500-seat theatre, outline proposals for no rooms larger than 100 seats.

While these figures are in part due to the small initial size of the new universities they are also a reflection of the change in teaching structure which underlies most of their programmes and has been termed 'the revolt against departmentalism'.[3]

The essence of this has been to establish a new type of degree course overlapping quite separate disciplines and organised into 'Schools of Study'.[4] At the University of York, for instance, courses arranged in such Schools will involve the association of subjects usually classified as belonging to separate faculties, e.g. Physics, Biology, Chemistry, so that students can take one as a main subject, one as a subsidiary. At the University of Essex it is initially planned to have three schools:

Physical Sciences   Social Studies   Comparative Studies

The School of Physical Sciences is to have an intake of approximately 560 per year by 1973 when the U/G population reaches 3,000. Within this structure it is aimed to have a common course for the first year followed by the split up into specialisations. Commenting on this new academic programme the Vice-Chancellor of Essex said:[5] 'We shall keep the traditional lecture to transmit facts and ideas and we hope enthusiasm. It will have a special place in the first-year scheme of study for scientists where it is essential to lay down principles and give a general view of the different subjects . . . we shall allow these lectures to grow large.'

In addition to this modification of departments into Schools of Study the new universities have also placed emphasis on the recommendation of the Committee for Higher Education that the first year of study should be seen in a broader context.[6] This then allows students a greater flexibility to move from one course to another within the Sciences and Technology after their initial year, and helps to meet some of the criticisms of the traditional first-degree courses, e.g.

> Courses overloaded
> Courses not suited to many students who take them
> Less rigid divisions between the sciences now

These initial statements towards a new pattern of teaching organisation indicate the widening of requirements for university building and the likely change in context for the lecture room. Already, for instance, in the sciences the concept of building non-

---

1. This information was supplied by the Planning Officers of the universities concerned and represented the academic policy at that time. Smaller flat floored classrooms have not been included.
2. Bibl. 53, p. 34.   3. Bibl. 38, p. 234.   4. Bibl. 43, p. 108.
5. Bibl. 6, p. 47.   6. Bibl. 3, p. 95.

designated general space to encourage academic flexibility has gained widespread acceptance (see Chapter 2, Section *b*).

At the same time the particular teaching role of the science lecture room is also being widened and further impetus given to methods of lecturing with the use of sophisticated audio-visual techniques. Recent additions to the types of teaching aid generally available for lecture room use include:

> The overhead writing and drawing projector
> Closed circuit television systems

Together with established forms, such as film or slide projection, they provide the lecturer with the opportunity to put across his information to maximum effect, especially if the lecture room is designed from the start with their co-ordinated use in mind. Where in America, in a series of experiments for the military training programmes, this has been developed in detail it has been possible to arrange for the simultaneous projection of three different images, the control of sequencing of images by push button from the lecturer's desk and the possibility for students to dial at random for stored information during the lecture.[1]

The combination of audio-visual aids can be taken in this way to reach a degree of presentation complexity which becomes a complete performance in its own right and in which the lecturer is reduced to the role of commentator or sequencer. Where this happens virtually a new technique emerges and either some redefinition of the lecture is necessary or else a separate teaching form must be recognised.

Primary amongst such areas of possible redefinition is the emerging use of television as a teaching medium and one which should not be confused with television just as a visual aid to teaching. For example:

1   Television as a visual aid

Television was first used as a lecture aid in hospitals where it could be mounted over an operating table, could be remote controlled and did not intrude into the field of activity. From there it was a logical step to its use for science lectures where it permits the demonstration of material too small or to inconvenient to show in the conventional teaching situation, e.g.:

Specimens in microscope set up from a selected viewpoint.

Complex and heavy apparatus outside the lecture room either in laboratories or other buildings linked by CCTV.

Teaching of special operating or handling skills.

Extensions of this type of use also allow the lecturer to show slides, and excerpts of film on the television screen or focus on apparatus, models or drawings to give a closeness of view not possible to a solitary 'live' observer.[2] The same methods can equally well be applied to laboratory teaching.

2   Television as a teaching medium.

A simple application of television in this way is to provide for overflow lectures. The overflow audience watches a lecture on the television screen in another room either in the same building or at a distance. The whole form of the lecture is therefore seen as a film presentation and the actual sense of contact with lecturer and place is removed. This is, however, only a temporary expedient

---

1. Bibl. 14, p. 72.
2. The television camera can in fact be used to cover all the main visual aids processes, i.e. it can show films, slides, still pictures (as epidiascope) or lecturers writing (as overhead projector). Only technical problems of lack of definition of screen image and the absence of an economically viable substitute for small monitor sets (i.e. cheap large screen presentation) as yet prevents its use in the lecture room as a single comprehensive aid.

and if this film presentation is to be really successful as teaching it must be produced with the viewing audience in mind, not just thought of as a lecture contained within the originating room. Television teaching origination becomes as a result a separate and distinct process which will allow for maximum effectiveness of the medium whether by CCTV, or OCTV on an educational network.

A brief comparison with American practice shows how the influence of commercial and educational networks has meant that television teaching has become highly organised to give a well directed and rehearsed production under studio conditions using the best teacher and aids available. The television camera 'looking-in' on the traditional lecture gives way to a whole new method.

Advantages of television as a medium for teaching include:

Allows lecture to be recorded and repeated as often as necessary.

Good lecturers can improve their performance with the help of extra staff and facilities not available in the ordinary lecture room.

A much wider range of visual aids can be integrated into the lecture without distraction to the audience.

The lecture can be originated in the most suitable place, e.g. a factory which an audience could not otherwise reach.

Teaching recorded outside the university or being originated in another university can be used.

In contrasting these alternative applications of television to university teaching the relevance can be seen for room and teaching group size. With the use of CCTV as an aid, an extra means of presenting visual information is at the lecturer's disposal and entirely under his control. The general case for sizes of lecture and limits for reasonable communication remains unaltered and only the detailed design of the lecture room to ensure optimum viewing of images needs extra consideration.

If however the major function is to teach by a total television presentation then for the students being taught the alternatives are:

1   To see it as one group (studies suggest that to make any CCTV production for less than 200 to 250 students will be uneconomic).[1]
2   To be broken up into a series of groups, either with reference to convenient room size and course structure or to provide for useful discussion group sizes after the television presentation. If broken up into groups these can also be enabled to see the presentation at different times.
3   To watch the presentation on individual television receivers either in their own rooms or in self-study carrells in the teaching building. Students can either play back a recorded lecture whenever convenient or else watch when transmitted by CCTV or OCTV.

Research to date does not suggest that there is any significant difference in student learning between those seeing television in a small group and those in a large one. The decision on size of group will rest rather with the alternatives listed above and with the general pattern of television teaching which has requirements for discussion after presentation, 'talk back' facilities to teacher or need for an audience in the originating studio. For example a science presentation to 400 students using television as the medium of teaching could equally well be given in one room with suitable viewing characteristics or in ten small rooms each with a monitor television set (40 is a reasonable maximum number for viewing a 27 in. screen). It could also be given in one or a series of standard science lecture rooms, provided that they were suitably equipped for

1. Bibl. 10, p. 71.

receiving and display, just as it could originate from a lecture room with special modifications (e.g. to lighting) if a correctly designed originating studio was not available.

While overlap solutions such as these latter may be strongly arguable on cost grounds for a small university, or one without a television service, it is important to recognise that for:

Lecture rooms using television as an aid
Rooms presenting teaching by television

the size, and design, of spaces required for each will be generated by separate sets of conditions.

The case often put in favour of using television far more as a teaching medium relates to its use for transmitting facts. In the sciences the broader based courses already referred to for the first year of undergraduate teaching have, as one of their main functions, to teach facts and remove the disparity between qualifying students drawn from different schools and teaching patterns. A wider use of pre-recorded or outside originated television here would support the point made by the Educational Facilities Laboratories in the U.S.A.:[1] 'with teaching talent in short supply we can no longer waste professors on mere exposition of facts. Increasingly they will deal with values, concepts, the meaning of it all—in very large groups or very small. More and more students will get "The facts" from inanimate dispensers—books, films, tapes, television and teaching machines—rather than from living teachers.'

By relieving some of the existing teaching pressures new methods, such as these, might allow for slightly fewer lectures but of a higher standard by giving staff more time for their preparation. This suggests that the role of the lecture would be strengthened rather than overshadowed by the use of new teaching methods. Where however the lecture has traditionally always been the central teaching method it now can be seen rather as one of a series of parallel methods each of which has its own relevance and its own particular requirements in terms of buildings and spaces.

In his book on *Campus Planning in the U.S.A.* Richard Dober suggests that the evolution in varieties of teaching spaces will continue and lists what he feels might become a common pattern on all campuses:[2]

Self-study alcoves	In library, special building or dormitories
Seminar rooms	Increasingly important if 'Team' teaching methods are adopted
Interchangeable classrooms	With possibility of subdivision and amalgamations
Lecture demonstration rooms	As above but with extra facilities
Special purpose classroom laboratories	For laboratory work involving specialised equipment
Multi-purpose classroom laboratories	As above but simple equipment and more subject interchangeability
Special teaching laboratories	

To this growing range of interior spaces must also be added the new forms of multiple function teaching buildings (see also Chapter 2, Section *b*), e.g.:

Lecture room block	Grouping of lecture and classrooms sharing common users and facilities and allowing for high utilisation; provision for receiving closed-circuit television services

1. Bibl. 13, p. 178.   2. Bibl. 49, p. 67.

Audio-visual classroom and studio building	Groups of rooms designed for optimum presentation of television and allied visual aids together with originating studios, rehearsal rooms, administrative and technical offices
Television centre	As above, with full originating and administrative facilities, but without actual presentation rooms; used rather as the focus of a university television service producing programmes for transmission to receiving points on the campus or in other universities
'Learning centre'	Combining areas of self-paced teaching machine booths with study carrells, seminar and classrooms; makes extensive use of audio-visual communications network and outside originated or stored television teaching

Any university plans of the future will have to allow for some, or a combination, of these varieties of teaching building and spaces. Design decisions will need to recognise not only what the importance of each category is but also how the use of the lecture room relates to it and what areas of common teaching activity exist.

For the sciences, where there appears to be a continuing case for direct pacing lectures[1] in parellel to the growing emphasis on small group and self-teaching methods (see Chapter 1, Section *a*), the provision of contact with the lecturer and the up-to-date interpretation of new material[2] may be seen as one item in the function of a 'university teaching centre'. By very definition the lecture and its presentation technique will be different from the smaller discussion group and, to be viable, will need to be in the size range which can be termed intermediate, i.e. on average from 80 to 160 with larger groups as academic structure, staff to student ratio or course size dictates.

Although any such 'teaching centre' would represent the assemblage of different teaching methods serving all disciplines, its physical form need not be considered as just one building but rather as a group of functionally linked and interdependent building units. As a result the provision of spaces to meet the need for science lectures could well be seen as one (or a series) of these units centrally administered by the university but planned in detail along with their related areas of teaching or research laboratories.

1. Bibl. 5, p. 53.   2. Bibl. 7, p. 53.

2. THE ARCHITECTURAL CONTEXT

a. Historical Evolution

During the mid-nineteenth century the *Dictionary of Architecture* published in London was able to define the Lecture Room as:[1] 'The place in which a professor instructs his audience, which is accommodated with seats placed either on a level, or on a plane more or less inclined, according to the province of the lecturer; a gallery is also sometimes provided when a large number of seats has to be obtained. In hospitals and similar places it is requisite that the seats should rise very rapidly. A professor's room and an assistant's room are generally necessary adjuncts to the lecture room.'

The Dictionary also referred its readers to a contemporary handbook on acoustics for the architect by T. Roger Smith which states:[2] 'Almost all modern theatres for dramatic performances have abandoned the stepped arrangement of seats... but there has risen up a class of buildings more nearly analogous than these to the ancient models—these are lecture theatres, often termed though without perfect accuracy, amphitheatres.'

At that time the two most widely known examples in England of this type of lecture room were those for the Royal College of Physicians by Sir Christopher Wren (Fig. 1*a*) and the then recently completed addition to the Royal Institution (Fig. 1*b*). The former was a regular sixteen-sided space of 40 ft internal diameter with steeply raked seats on all sides, and the lecture table in the centre. Writing of its function, in his *Life of Wren* of 1823, James Elmes says:[3] 'The interior—is one of the best imagined for seeing, hearing and classification of the students and fellows, and for the display of anatomical demonstrations or philosophical experiments upon a table in the middle of the arena.'

This primary intention to show scientific demonstration lectures to the best advantage was also the basis of the design for the Royal Institution theatre where there is a semicircular plan with principal dimensions height:depth:breadth of 30 ft:45 ft:60 ft (2:3:4).[4] The theatre has always been considered as extremely successful for the single speaker partly perhaps due to the minimum room volume per place achieved and partly due to the setting out of the room section on an 'isacoustic' curve. This represented an early application of the method of setting out the seats in any large building to provide direct sight and sound paths from audience to speaker by allowing a consistent sight clearance of one row above the row in front (producing the characteristic concave floor section).

In analysing this section at the Royal Institution for his handbook, Smith notes the importance that must be attached at the design stage to deciding whether the audience has to look down on a demonstration table or merely at the speaker, i.e. what the teaching function is to be. He also notes the disadvantage of the semicircular plan in that the audience to either side of the speaker suffered poor conditions for seeing and hearing. A similar point was made later by Gaudet where in his analysis of building types[5] he argued that it is not possible to watch satisfactorily an experiment from an oblique angle. As this represented a contradiction to the rule of focusing lines of sight

1. Bibl. 18, vol. v, p. 56.   2. Bibl. 66, p. 101.   3. Bibl. 17, p. 451.
4. Bibl. 66, p. 103.   5. Bibl. 65, p. 261.

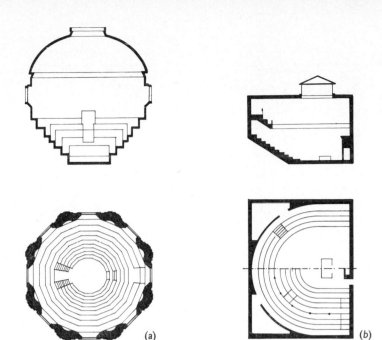

(a)

(b)

Fig. 1 (a). Lecture theatre of the College of Physicians, London, by Wren, 1689. From James Elmes. (b). Lecture theatre at the Royal Institution London as built 1840. From T. Roger Smith.

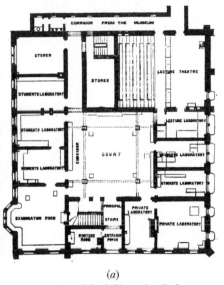

(a)

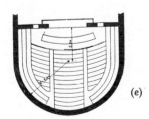

(b)

Fig. 2 (a). The original Clarendon Laboratory, Oxford, as built for the Department of Physics. The lecture room embedded in the University Science Building in this way was to become the established pattern. Plan and elevation from Builder 1869. (b). Exterior.

(a)

(a)

(b)

(c)

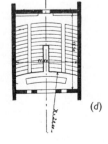

(d)

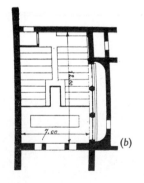

(e)

Fig. 3. Lecture theatre planforms recommended by Gaudet in his *Elements et Théorie de L'Architecture* of 1909. (a). Non-Designated. (b). Physiology. (c). Geology. (d). Physics. (e). Chemistry.

in plan to a point and forming a semicircular layout he suggested that for lecture rooms a general rule for planning should be:

Semicircle   Arts, literary subjects
Rectangle   Science

This would still allow the classical amphitheatre form to remain for an orator addressing a large audience but would provide for more technical subjects to have rooms suited to their special needs.

While he then proceeded to make detailed exceptions to this rule, Gaudet's review is interesting in that it confirms how, by the end of the nineteenth century, the lecture theatre had assumed its position as a new and distinctive element in all types of university teaching building, and particularly where the scientific subjects were concerned. This was due not so much to the example of the earlier theatres in specialised institutions but rather to the upsurge of university building in the late nineteenth century which provided unified premises for teaching and for the first time gave accommodation to the new branches of scientific research.

Early examples in the U.K. of separate buildings for university science departments included the Cavendish Laboratories, Cambridge (1874) and the Clarendon Laboratories, Oxford (1869) (Fig. 2a, b).[1] Both were for Physics and at the Clarendon an 'experimental' lecture theatre (150), a theoretical lecture room and laboratory places for forty reflected a teaching course structure divided into three parts:

1   Experimental lectures on the principles of science
2   Mathematical lectures on the physical theories
3   Practical studies of experimental methods

Where a completely new foundation was being built such as Owens College, Manchester[2] (later the University), the design was often evolved as a single building complex housing administrative and academic accommodation with embedded lecture theatres for various disciplines (an architectural arrangement which perhaps reached its grandest expression in Nenot's new building for the Sorbonne, Paris, of 1895).[3] Similar new colleges were founded in most of the large civic centres, e.g. Newcastle, Leeds, Bristol, Nottingham, and provided the nucleus of the later civic universities. Most were on 'in-town' sites and principles of planning for any future expansion were virtually non-existent. Even where at Cambridge and Oxford large areas were set aside for the development of the sciences no consistent plan was established and buildings were thought of individually and added at random when required.

The architectural form of the lecture room, with its large volume often running through two storeys and its stepped section, did not receive any particular recognition in the designs of the late nineteenth century and early twentieth century. It was not until the re-thinking of architectural principles after the 1920s, together with popularising of the functionalist attitude to building, that the universities as clients were prepared to accept, or architects to offer, designs which expressed the lecture room as a distinct form within the planning programme.

Individual projects which helped to establish this change in architectural attitude included those by the Russian Constructivist school, Le Corbusier and Walter Gropius. In all the now familiar trapezoidal planform and raked section were shown for the first time as separate and identifiable volumes (Figs. 4a–c).

1. Bibl. 19, p. 369.   2. Bibl. 20, p. 85.
3. Bibl. 65, p. 258.

[*Photo AD*

(*a*). University of Leicester, Engineering Department. Architects: Stirling and Gowan, 1964.

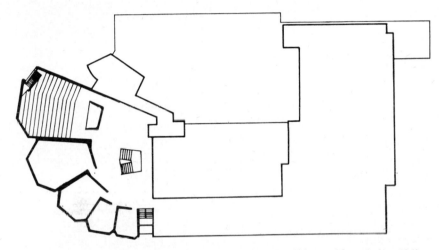

[*Photo Girsberger*

(*b*). Project for the Palace of the Soviets. Le Corbusier, 1931.

(*c*). Lecture theatres forming part of cultural centre Wolfsburg. Alvar Aalto, 1962.

Fig. 4. The lecture theatre expressed as an element in the programme.

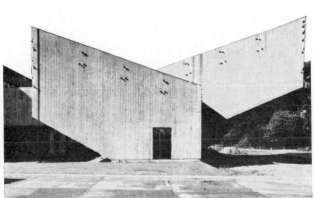

[*Photo AR*

(*a*). University of Hull. Lecture theatres attached to Department of Physics. Architects: Co-Partnership, 1964.

[*Photo Thames and Hudson*

(*b*). Lecture theatre New York University. Architect: Marcel Breuer.

Fig. 5. The lecture theatre emphasized as a sculptural form.

Since that time and particularly in England during the university expansion programmes of the 1950s and 1960s the form of the lecture room has become an almost mandatory adjunct for any major university science building. While this is partly due to a reversal of nineteenth-century architectural principles coupled with an excessive desire to have points of sculptural 'interest', it also reflects a basic functional development in the requirements of science teaching areas (Figs. 5*a*, *b*).

At its simplest this requires that a departmental building should be considered as a standard, repetitive structural system giving the user the chance to alter arrangements and expand laboratory spaces.[1] At its most complex it suggests that a whole science area be considered in a similar way as an area of flexible and easily serviced space.[2] In either case the architect is given the strongest argument to extract awkward, non-standard volumes from the basic teaching buildings and relate them as separate units.

Parallel to this need for more general purpose space within buildings, there has been a change in the planning of the lecture room. Apart from highly specialised rooms, e.g. for Physiology and Anatomy the science lecture room has come to be designed to an almost general specification with variations only in its servicing and equipping. The range of possible planforms given by Gaudet (Fig. 3)[3] has evolved into the room which can provide for

> Experiments on a demonstration bench for frontal viewing
> Use of front wall for chalkboard and diagrams
> Projection of slides and cine screen images

The principal agent for this change has been the increasing use of visual aids and in particular the ability to make and show easily 35 mm slides. The equipment to do this has progressed from the introduction of the large early carbon arc projectors to the latest remote controlled, portable and long throw (pulse light) models.

The most important architectural implications have therefore centred around the need to obtain satisfactory conditions for teaching with projected images (including the need for 'blacking out'). As a result the majority of new science lecture rooms in the U.K. are being designed without opening windows and day lighting (see Chapter 6, Section *a*) and instead are providing a controlled environment with efficient mechanical heating and ventilation and high levels of artificial illumination. Not only do such methods now make windowless conditions widely acceptable and more efficient for viewing visual aids but they also enable the lecture theatre to be designed to improved comfort conditions allowing for continuous teaching use.

As a category of teaching space the science lecture theatre has therefore been proving progressively more sophisticated, more critically designed and necessarily more expensive. The realisation of this has made universities anxious to make better use of their lecture facilities,[4] and rooms are now being increasingly planned for shared use by several departments in order to achieve higher standards of plant efficiency.

1. Bibl. 81. In particular the contribution of Sir Eric Ashby on the Design of Teaching Laboratories, p. 6.
2. Bibl. 50, p. 595.
3. Bibl. 65, p. 267.
4. A combination of this desire for high utilisation together with the need to provide for varying audience sizes has produced several designs for divisible lecture rooms. So far, however, this method of achieving greater room use has had as its main obstacle the unsatisfactory sound insulation values given by any economic form of movable partition. (See, for instance, Bibl. 84, p. 170.)

b. New Building Types

The scale of expansion planned (1964) for new universities in England is indicated by proposals[1] for their student populations:

	1974–75	Eventual population
Essex	3,000	10,000 to 20,000
Lancaster	3,000	7,000
Warwick	5,000	15,000 to 20,000
York	3,000	6,000 to 7,000
Kent	3,000	6,000

By contrast the creation of five new universities in California is planned (1964) for a much faster rate:[2]

	1974–75	Eventual population
Los Angeles (S.C.)	10,000	20,000
San Bernadino (S.C.)	8,000	20,000
San Diego (U.C.)	7,500	27,500
Orange Co. (U.C.)	12,500	27,500
S. Central Coast (U.C.)	10,000	27,500

In Germany projected new universities populations are:

Bremen	6,000
Bochum	10,000
Dortmund	6,000
Regensberg	5,000
Constance	3,000
Berlin[3]	10,000

and major expansion is planned for eight other existing foundations. The T.H. Stuttgart and T.H. Aachen, which are to be increased from 6,000 to 10,000 population, are typical examples of these latter and demonstrate how the lack of space for expansion on their existing town centre sites is forcing the whole of the science and research areas to be detached and replanned on new and unrestricted out-of-town sites.

The general philosophy of planning for such new universities and expansion areas has had to recognise a change in attitude for future building. This has been conditioned by the rapid increase in the space needs of science and technology and the difficulty in forecasting any future patterns of development. Emerging design principles for the sciences are:

1   Any planning must provide for future growth, change or contraction of scientific disciplines. Building solutions must provide for the interaction between disciplines and must have a deliberate flexibility capable of being adapted to meet such inter- action or change. As noted by Professor Asa Briggs when he wrote of university

1. It should be noted that the rate of growth of the existing English civic universities has seen a repeated pattern of steadily increasing upper limits for proposed maximum size. An example of this growth can be seen from Liverpool:

2,500 students in	1944
3,500	1946 (post-Barlow report)
5,000	1954
7,000	1960
10,000	1964 (post-Robbins report)

The full emphasis of the Robbins report may in fact produce a period of expansion from 1973/74 which will be a further heavy loading on to these established universities.
2. See Bibl. 39, p. 96; 42, p. 175; 57, p. 112.
3. For details of competition winning entry see Bibl. 45, p. 380.

design for the 1960s:[1] 'Early decisions will have a tremendous influence on the whole pattern of the future—(there is needed) a proper plan of growth relating building plans to academic growth.'

2   Space to be built in universities for science use must be considered in general terms, not as individual buildings each for a particular subject and with a completely separate identity but rather on the basis of speculative office space which can be rented as required.[2]

3   Within any university the various categories of building each belong on a scale or hierarchy of permanence. At one end of the scale temporary spaces for research or experiment represent the shortest life span or the one most likely to need adaptation. At the other the student-living areas represent a function which has not altered its basic requirements since the Middle Ages and which is a structuring element in any plan least likely to change.[3] A simple range might be:

> Research/light industrial—least predictable
> Teaching laboratories
> Communal buildings
> Arts teaching areas
> Seminar/small cell buildings
> Study bedrooms/living—least changing

This hierarchy of transience, together with an analysis of the space and servicing needs of different activities, form major generating items in any university programme. For science developments they will separate those activities which need flexible space from those at a higher level of permanence.

As well as this requirement for greater flexibility in science teaching buildings the lessening of departmental division and the more general use of science lecture theatres have all been noted. Their combined influence on university planning attitudes has helped to produce a new building type: the science lecture theatre block.

Although large groups of central lecture rooms, and more particularly classrooms, have long been established for shared use in the Arts subjects (Fig. 6), it was not until the 1950s that definite proposals were made for comparable buildings for the sciences (Figs. 7*a–d*). Typical programmes that have emerged for these lecture blocks provide a total capacity of upwards of 2,000 student places and may include a high proportion of small (under 100 capacity) rooms for the mathematics teaching which is a heavy load allied to the sciences (see Chapter 5). The categories of space that have formed the basis for design are:

> Lecture rooms and classrooms
> Preparation, Projection and Plant areas
> Cloakrooms, W.C.s and Janitor's room
> Circulation areas and Foyers

In this type of building, with a high percentage of students moving around at change-over times, the foyer and circulation space can be seen as perhaps the most important generating element in design (see Chapter 7). A further aspect of this function was emphasised by an article on 'Architecture and the Sociology of University Life' in which Michael Cassidy noted:[4] 'Students from different departments, schools of study or

1. Bibl. 38, p. 235.
2. See, for instance, the architectural solution proposed for the Oxford University Science Area, Bibl. 50, p. 595.
3. See Bibl. 38, p. 289, where Michael Brawne discusses the implications of such a hierarchy on the design of student accommodation.
4. Bibl. 4, p. 353.

Fig. 6. The lecture block for the Arts at Sidgwick Avenue, Cambridge. Architects: Casson and Conder, 1960.

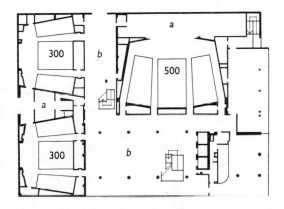

[*Photo AR*

(*a*). Manchester College for Science and Technology. Ground Floor Plan 1:1000. *a*, Preparation. *b*, Foyer. Architects: Cruikshank and Seward, 1962.

(*b*). Manchester College for Science and Technology. Exterior showing small lecture rooms and mathematics teaching rooms above podium.

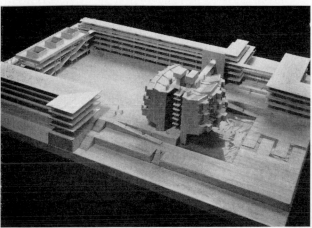

[*Photo University of Leeds*

(*c*). University of Leeds. Project 1963 from Development Plan Review. Architects: Chamberlin Powell and Bon.

(*d*). T. H. Delft. Lecture theatres and auditorium maximum. Architects: van den Broek and Bakema, 1965.

Fig. 7. Designs for the Science Lecture Block.

whatever will meet officially—will queue before lectures, share seminars and have coffee together. This contact must be optimised. How can the architect contribute towards the productivity of these contacts. By making the lecture or seminar room comfortable of course, but also by considering the spaces immediately outside.'

He went on to suggest the use of adjacent areas where discussions after lectures could continue and also pointed out the importance of planning for the lecture room so that exits and circulation ways flowed through an identifiable central foyer and meeting area.

These ideas apply all the more strongly if greater emphasis is put on the use of separate centralised common user teaching buildings and the amount of time spent there by the student is increased. If, for instance, the lecture grouping needs to be made more complex in the future to house not only lecture rooms but also seminar, tutorial and self-study spaces then the chances of optimising contact will improve and need to be provided for in design.

While these first science lecture blocks were being planned, the use of new teaching media for higher education in the U.S.A. was also producing programmes for other large and distinctive central building forms[1] (see Chapter 1, Section *b*). For example:

Classroom and Studio Building, University of Miami, Florida.[2]

This contains within an octagonal planform eight theatres at 300 each of wedge shape with ramped floors and tapering walls to a 10 ft square television viewing screen. This room arrangement is considered to give much better focus than the usual lecture room and is made possible because the principal role is viewing rather than the presentation by lecturer, chalkboard or experiment. Rooms are centred on a back projection area and allied spaces include ETV studios and administration offices (Fig. 8*a*).

Instructional Communications Centre, Rensellaer Polytechnic Institute, Troy, N.Y.[3]

This was the subject of a 1963 architectural competition for a building design aimed mainly at the use of ETV. The projected design has 1 at 450 and 4 at 150 lecture rooms together with back projection areas, administration, studios for film and television, workshops, and exhibition area (Fig. 8*b*).

Learning Centre, Grand Valley State College, Michigan.[4]

Building unit proposed of 30,000 sq.ft has 256 teaching carrells each of which has access to seventeen video and eighty audio information channels. Associated conference rooms (2) for groups of 64 and a divisible lecture hall for 186 mean that a total of 572 students can be taught in the building and it is planned that they spend half their time in carrells and half in other learning activities.

In addition detailed architectural studies have been made in the U.S.A. for the Ford Foundation and the Educational Facilities Laboratories on the design of lecture and auditorium spaces.[5] These have been aimed at establishing satisfactory conditions for the presentation and origination, with studio techniques, of television teaching (Fig. 8*c*).

The impact of new teaching methods requiring building spaces such as those above has yet to be seen in universities in the U.K. Certainly, the television centre requiring a building for the technical and academic origination is likely to be increasingly a new element in development plans (e.g. at University of Leeds). For the sciences the need for new media may be more limited than for the arts but they will still be required to meet the increasing pressures of teaching basic factual information to first-year students.

1. Bibl. 48, p. 41.   2. Bibl. 75, pt. II, p. 46.   3. Bibl. 13, p. 178.
4. Bibl. 14, p. 69.   5. Bibl. 75, pt. III.

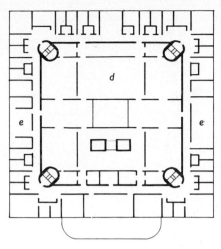

First floor

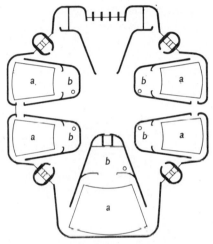

Ground floor

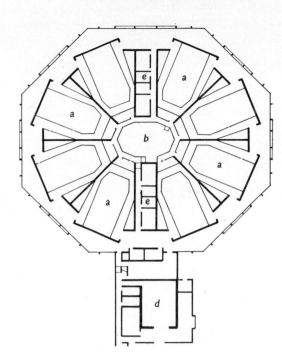

(*a*). Classroom and studio building University of Miami, Florida. Auditoria of 300 capacity with ramped floors. Scale 1:1000.

(*b*). Instructional communications centre. Rensellaer Polytechnic Institute, New York. Auditoria 1 at 450 and 4 at 150. Scale 1:1000.

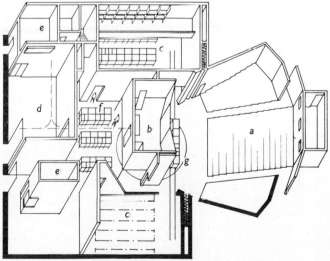

(*c*). A design study shown in 'New Spaces for Learning' aimed at providing satisfactory conditions for television origination and presentation together with maximum utilisation.

Fig. 8. Designs for buildings to use new teaching media in higher education.

a, Auditorium.
b, Back Projection Area.
c, Preparation Area.
d, Studio Presentation Area.
e, Offices.
f, Modular Trolleys.
g, Turntable.

Spaces required for this, either in the form of teaching carrell laboratories or television viewing rooms, will have to be incorporated in the science area. This could be:

> In standard teaching areas
> As separate buildings
> Allied to existing central teaching facilities
>   (e.g. science lecture blocks, library)

By taking some of the load off first-year lectures and also by their possible need for physical amalgamation with groups of lecture rooms, these new spaces for learning may as a result call into question the present architectural role of the single central lecture block. This will not be because the lectures themselves are not still needed but because this building type represents:

1 A finite organisation of rooms with little opportunity for future addition or alteration.
2 A design originated at one moment (even if constructed later in stages) and therefore giving little possibility for changes of programme in response to developments in the academic pattern.[1]
3 A heavy concentration of building space and weight of student numbers (especially so if allied to extra teaching spaces outlined above).

Together with the greater reliance of the new universities on small group teaching spaces this suggests that rather than one lecture block as a central teaching building the likely emergent form for the sciences may need to be a series of smaller groupings providing for a variety of lecture and related spaces and with more flexibility for growth or alteration. Not only would such a pattern reflect the change in emphasis of the lecture from a primary teaching method to one of a range of methods, but it would also allow for an architectural planning system to be evolved whereby such groupings could be inserted into the various phases of a basic science area framework as needed (see Chapter 5).

1. The central lecture block at the University of Leeds as designed in detail by 1962 had 21 rooms at 1,690 places. To meet the likely expansion policy proposed by the Committee on Higher Education it has already had to be redesigned to provide 25 rooms at 2,650 places. See Bibl. 52, p. 206.

II

PLANNING FOR THE
SCIENCE LECTURE ROOM

3. LOCATION AND SIZE OF ROOMS IN THE U.K.

The number of universities and university colleges in England with full-time students during the academic year 1963–64 was twenty-two. Of these the new universities of York and East Anglia were only receiving full-time students for the first year and the other recent foundation of Sussex had under 1,000 students.

The total number of full-time students reading for their first degree in these twenty-two universities was 96,077. Together with 30,368 students in Scotland and Wales the total full-time student population in the U.K. was 126,445.[1]

For the universities in England the more detailed allocation of these full-time students by faculties for 1963–64 was:[2]

	Numbers	Percentage
Arts	28,610	29·8
Social Studies	13,256	13·8
Pure Science	26,364	27·4
Applied Science	13,864	14·3
Medicine } Dentistry }	11,883	12·4
Agriculture } Veterinary }	2,100	2·3
Total	96,077	100·0

In order to examine the pattern of existing departmental lecture room accommodation for the Pure Sciences a survey was made of seven established universities:

	Student population	
	1964[3]	Planned for 1970s[4]
Birmingham	4,982	6,300
Bristol	4,000	6,500
Cambridge	9,170	
Durham	1,914	3,000
Manchester	5,908	8,900
Newcastle	4,402	6,000
Nottingham	3,067	5,500

This survey[5] was able to provide detailed information on the size, location (see Figs. 9a–g), use and design of all rooms in use or completed during the academic year 1964–65 in the categories:

Biological Sciences   Physical Sciences
Chemical Sciences   Geological Sciences

1. Bibl. 44, p. 1.   2. Ibid. p. 25, Table 5.   3. Ibid. p. 12, Table 1.
4. Figures reported by individual universities and based on expansion proposed by the Committee for Higher Education in 1963.
5. To ensure that information obtained was complete and to a uniform basis, a visit was made to all the lecture rooms in the survey. This enabled a standard proforma to be filled in at the buildings concerned and to be checked with the assistance of the administrative staff. In this way it was possible to build up an 'identity card' for each lecture room with the required details and with a photographic record of main interior features.

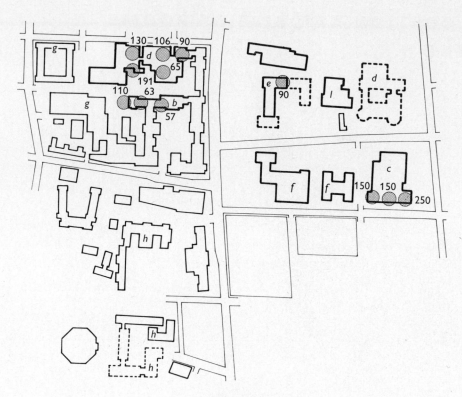

(*a*). Manchester.

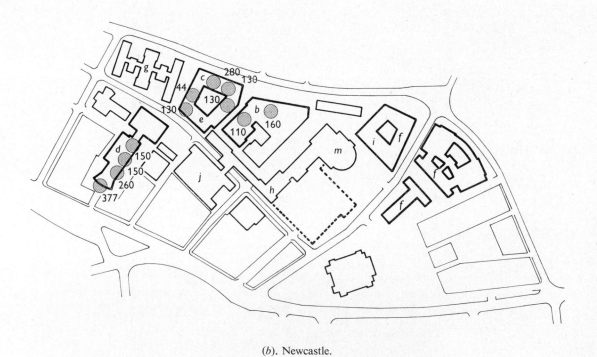

(*b*). Newcastle.

Fig. 9. The location and size of lecture rooms for the Natural Sciences in Survey of English Universities, 1964–65.

a, Natural Sciences.

b, Natural Sciences: Botany, Zoology.

c, Natural Sciences: Chemistry.

d, Natural Sciences: Physics.

e, Natural Sciences: Geology.

f, Technology, Applied Sciences.

g, Medicine.

h, Arts, Social Sciences.

i, Mathematics.

j, Student and Staff Facilities.

k, Student Residence.

l, Lecture Block.

m, Library.

☐ Science and Technology Buildings.

⬤ Science Lecture Rooms.

☐ Other University Buildings.

Scale 1:5000.

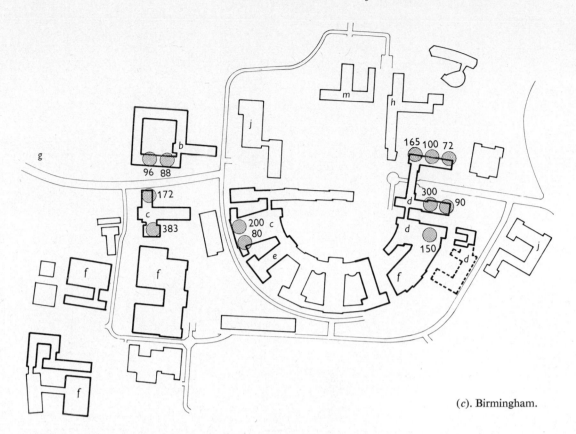

(*c*). Birmingham.

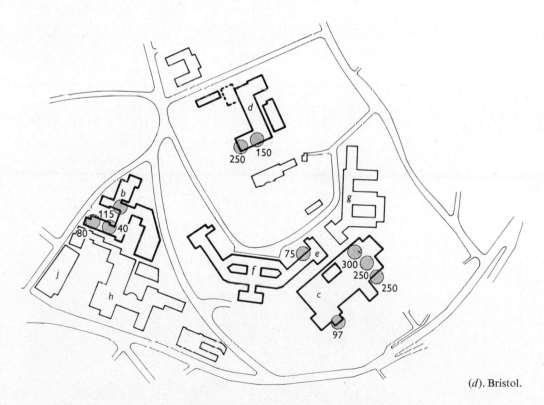

(*d*). Bristol.

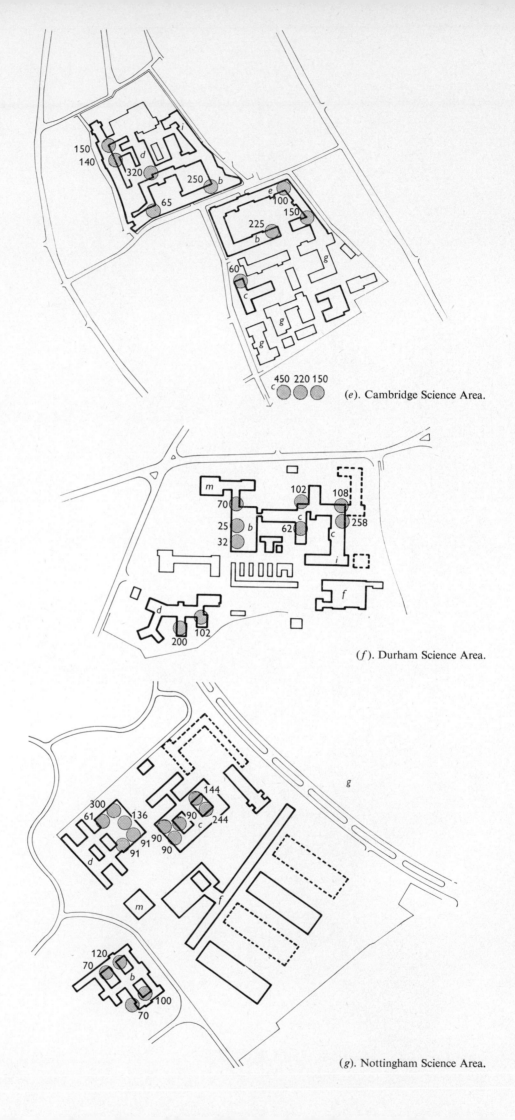

(e). Cambridge Science Area.

(f). Durham Science Area.

(g). Nottingham Science Area.

In the following table the number and capacity of these rooms has been shown against the available 1963–64 full-time student population for the pure sciences:

University	Science[1] students	Lecture rooms	Lecture places	Places per student
Birmingham	1,375	12	1,896	1·4
Bristol	1,038	10	1,607	1·6
Cambridge	2,726	12	2,280	0·84
Durham	677	9	959	1·4
Manchester	1,522	12	1,452	0·96
		(14)*	(2,182)	(1·4)
Newcastle	1,088	11	1,544	1·4
Nottingham	1,063	14	1,698	1·6

* Two lecture rooms (250, 480) have recently been built in a central 'lecture block'. They are available to any science department as well as for outside use and are not included in the survey by departmental groupings.

The definition of a lecture room is necessarily open to interpretation. For the above figures all rooms were included in the survey which were used for formal courses of lectures given as part of the main teaching curriculum. Only 5% of all rooms visited as recognised lecture rooms did in fact prove to be smaller than 60 in capacity and it was interesting that the majority of these had stepped floors.

The distribution of science lecture rooms by size groups for the seven universities was:

Under 50	51/100	101/200	201/300	301/400	over 400
3	26	31	13	6	1

Total 80 rooms: 11,800 places.

If this distribution is taken by closer increments of scale, e.g. for every 40 places (which corresponds to a common increment of laboratory group size) the pattern was:

Under 80	80/119	120/159	160/199	200/239	240/279	280/319	over 320
16	23	17	4	4	8	4	4

The distribution of rooms by subject groupings:

	Rooms	Places
Physics	27	4,388
Chemistry	27	4,816
Zoology/Botany	18	1,793
Others	8	803
Total	80	11,800

The location of these science lecture rooms within the universities followed a traditional pattern of individual rooms, or groups of two or three rooms, built into their departmental blocks when they were first established. In some cases additional rooms have been added to a building or provided in later extensions to the department. In new science areas such as Nottingham the intensity of groupings of departmental rooms is much higher and in one case, at Manchester, the next logical step of providing a central science lecture block has been taken. (In practice however the main bulk of this building of 20 at 80 seat classrooms is used almost entirely for Mathematics.)

1. Bibl. 44, p. 25, Table 5.

The age of rooms, which reflected the age of the various departmental buildings to which they belonged and in which they were embedded was:

Date*	Rooms	Percentage	Places
Pre-1914	19	23·8	2,512
1914 to 1945	7	8·7	988
Post-1945	54	67·5	8,300
Total	80	100·0	11,800

* Rooms converted completely at a later date are counted as at the date of conversion (three occurrences).

4. ROOM UTILISATION

a. Present Standards Compared

Of the 80 rooms comprising the Natural Sciences lecture accommodation of the seven U.K. Universities listed, information was available for 70 for the number of hours per week for which they were in use for timetabled lectures.[1] This varied from 3 h per week to a maximum of 23 h per week. The average over all rooms was 13·0 h occupancy per week.

The following table shows the frequency of occurrence of different room use levels:

Hours in use	To 5	6 7 8	9 10 11	12 13 14	15 16 17	18 19 20	21+
Occurrences	2	10	14	18	13	10	3

Although, as might be expected, the largest sizes of rooms showed a falling off in utilisation the general use of rooms by size categories showed little fluctuation:

Average size of room	40	80	120	160	200	240	280+
Average use (h per week)	14·4	13·0	14·0	12·4	14·2	13·1	10·0

The capacity of all rooms in this sample for utilisation (70) was 9,969 places; the total potential lecture place hours per week (Room Capacity × Room Use totalled up) was 125,983. This yielded an average figure of 12·7 h per week as the existing potential use of places in Natural Science lecture rooms (potential as not all seats in a lecture room will be filled).

The allocation of the working week for lecture use varies slightly between universities but is generally accepted at approx. 32 h. A typical pattern would be potential use of:

	M.	T.	W.	Th.	F.	S.
a.m. (h)	4	4	4	4	4	4
p.m. (h)	2	2	*	2	2	

* Free afternoon.

In other cases there may be no free or 'games afternoon' and Saturday morning lectures may be omitted or limited to 3 h.

At this level of room use the average of 13·0 h per week represents a general occupancy of lecture rooms for 40% of their possible timetabled use. Society and extra mural lectures which take place in some rooms in the evening from 6 p.m. have not been included nor has the quite frequent habit of using a large lecture room for an occasional seminar or tutorial due to lack of suitable accommodation elsewhere.

The variation in average use of departmental rooms by subject was:

	Hours per week
Physics	13·6
Chemistry	11·8
Botany/Zoology	12·9

1. Figures for spring term 1964 taken from timetables as held in departments or reported from central registries during the course of the survey.

Between the universities themselves there was a considerable variation in average use of lecture rooms from 9 h per week (min.) to 16 h per week (max.). This reflected not only the different pressures of student numbers but also differences in approach to time-tabling. In general science departments are responsible for their own lecture rooms and the use made of them will depend on the number of rooms available to that department and the need for lectures within the departmental timetable.

Some degree of central control may however be kept by the university to see when rooms are in use and in some cases lectures from other disciplines (usually arts) will be fitted in to available periods in science lecture rooms. A typical example of this is shown by a survey of lecture room utilisation in the Science area Cambridge (spring term 1964). All departments[1] after arranging their own timetabled lectures had been asked for a return of available accommodation to the University Registry so that arts lectures could if necessary be placed there. The analysis showed:

	Timetabled use per week for sciences*	Offered to Registry per week
20 lecture rooms (approx 3,000 places)	221 h	84 h

* Due to inadequate size of their own lecture rooms six departments were forced to give some of their lectures in rooms belonging to other sciences. These were recorded as use of room occupied. Information for 20/22 total rooms.

This represented an average use of rooms of 11 h (max. instance 19 h) in a timetable week of 34 h. Several departments had a value of 19 to 20 h per week for their own use plus that offered and saw no difficulties in rooms being used to these higher levels. The fact that the central Registry was unable to take up the majority of these offers does not alter the position that the potential of accommodation wasted in situations where rooms are separately under the control of individual departments can be high.

Comparable figures for the use of arts lecture theatres at Cambridge taken at the same time showed that for the two main groups of rooms:

Sidgwick Avenue (12 rooms)   Average use = 15 h per week
Mill Lane (12 rooms)   Average use = 14·4 h per week

However, figures on the use of lecture rooms in terms of hours of occupancy per week do not represent total efficiency of use of plant. In most cases lectures are nowhere near full either by falling off in attendance or more often because class sizes are not suited to room sizes available. This is demonstrated in the following space use surveys:

1   A survey of lecture rooms for Science and Technology carried out by the University of Leeds as material for the preparation of the 1960 Development plan:

Lecture theatres	Lecture places	Students expected*	Potential places†
30	2,729	24,888	48,256

* Programmed for but not necessarily all able to attend.
† Summation of Room sizes × Use in hours per week.

This showed that the lecture places in rooms used were only on average 52% occupied.

Average class size was 47 as opposed room size 91.

1. Anatomy, Veterinary Anatomy, Biochemistry, Botany, Inorganic Chemistry, Physical Chemistry, Chemical Engineering, Geology, Metallurgy, Mineralogy, Pathology, Pharmacology, Physiology, Physics, Psychology, Zoology.

2   A survey of Arts lecture rooms at University of Newcastle (then Kings College) in 1962 for the Percy Building:

Class size (average)	5	15	25	35	45	55	65	75	85
Frequency	56	54	38	26	10	19	3	5	2
Total	213 classes								

	Room size	10 and 12	20	40 and 48	108
	Frequency	11	25	145	32
	Total	213 classes			

Therefore classes totalled 5,185 (average) when 11,048 lecture places were in use which is an occupancy of 47%.

3   A survey of lecture rooms for Arts, Social Sciences and Law at the University of Hull in 1963 showed the following occupation of rooms:

Room size (average)	5	15	25	35	45	55	65	75	85	95	100+
Occupancy (percentage)	92	74	55	59	53	76	62	63	—	57	54

It was found that, in general, lecture rooms at Hull were in use for 60% of a possible 32 h timetable week at an occupancy of 60%.

Inquiries into the use of lecture rooms at Battersea College of Technology and Brunel College[1] in 1964 showed that lecture and classrooms were in use for an average of 30 h per week. At Brunel it was also found that average occupation was, however, only 50% and it was suggested that rather than having too many rooms of the same size, efficiency of plant use would have been better served if a wider range of rooms had allowed more choice of fit for classroom sizes. (Another case for flexibility for future room sizes was made as a result of the Hull survey when it was recommended that small rooms might be built now which could later be converted into larger units to meet the needs of expansion.)

A comparison of the present pattern of use in Great Britain with lecture rooms in Europe or U.S.A. at once emphasises the difference in the accepted student working week, i.e. the hours which regular courses of lectures are timetabled. The total possible in U.S.A. has been taken as high as 45 h per week for California;[2] in Germany the official (Wissenschaftsrates) recommendations have suggested 40 h per week.[3]

While these standards have been seriously questioned and are discussed later, in both cases the regular timetable day is taken as from 8 a.m. to 5 p.m. As a result use for lecture rooms of 30 h per week or more is often achieved.

Germany

At T.H. Aachen the use of the main group of lecture halls for Technology and Natural Sciences in 1965 was:

University	Subject	No. of rooms	Average use (hours per week)*
T.H. Aachen	Technology Nat. Sci.	9	37

* Present utilisation aimed at 30 h per week.

A wider survey of all lecture rooms at T.H. Aachen, made as part of a rebuilding and expansion study,[4] further found that the average class sizes came only to 25% of those

1. Universities designate.   2. Bibl. 56, p. 320, Table 30.   3. Bibl. 64, p. 14.   4. Bibl. 62, p. 10.

expected (i.e. who had 'signed' up as is usual in Germany for the course) and at any one time those actually attending may only amount to 80% of the potential.[1]

Figures for a variety of Natural Science lecture rooms (average size 441) surveyed in other German universities in 1963[2] showed examples of equally high use in hours per week:

Universities	Subject	No. of rooms	Average use (hours per week)
12	Nat. Sci.	15	25

At T.H. Stuttgart the Zentralarchivs bureau reported that the pressure for lecture space had become so great that an experimental timetable day for lectures from 7 a.m. to 8 p.m. had been tested out (13 h × 5 = 65 h per week). In practice use of rooms had often reached 100% but this was only possible by virtually continuous working, with no concessions to free afternoons, etc., and by central control and timetabling.

America

Considerable analysis of the use of facilities in universities and colleges has been made in California by the State Department of Education. In their 'Restudy' of 1955 an analysis of fifteen college campuses found that out of a timetabled week possible of 45 h the average use of classrooms ranged:[3]

> Minimum   19 h per week (42% efficiency)
> Maximum   38 h per week (84% efficiency)
> Average   27 h per week (60% efficiency)

(This latter figure would approximate to 19 h average use per week for the Great Britain timetable of 32 h.) The average class size, by enrolments, was given at the same time as 49%.

A more recent survey (1963) for all California's public institutions of higher education revealed the following utilisation for classrooms (lecture and seminar rooms):[4]

Institutions	No. of rooms	Room use (hours per week)	Occupancy
State Colleges	1,307	25·1	72%
University of California	689	27·1	57%

Comparative levels of classroom use for universities and colleges throughout the U.S.A. published in 1960 were:[5]

	Percentage rank	All institutions
Average number of	90	27·3
periods per week	50	19·1
Percentage places	90	63·5
occupied when rooms in use	50	55·0

b. Methods for Analysing Use

In recognising the existing high levels of pressures for lecture room accommodation both in Germany and the U.S.A. it had been found necessary to establish standards for their use both as minimum criteria and also as an aid to future planning. Contributions in both these countries towards the theory of university planning have recently been

1. Information from Institut fur Schulbau, Aachen.   2. Bibl. 76, Appendix.
3. Bibl. 56, p. 320.   4. Bibl. 58, p. 18, Table 6.   5. Quoted in Bibl. 58, p. 36, Table 10.

published and, in the absence of any established principles for determining utilisation of instructional buildings in England, it is valuable to examine these:

State of California

The series of studies that culminated in the Master Plan for Higher Education in California of 1960 saw the question of utilisation of instructional rooms of such importance that it was recommended:[1]

1 In scheduling classes greater use be made of late p.m. hours and if possible Saturday mornings.
2 Central control of instructional facilities and in particular the spaces used by more than one department (with special exceptions, e.g. medicine having highly specialised use).
3 Examination of four quarter (i.e. year round) use of University buildings. Each quarter to be of 12 weeks as used at Stanford University, University of Chicago, Washington University.

Minimum standards for room use proposed were:[2]

Classrooms	30 scheduled hours per week at 60% capacity
Teaching Laboratories	20 scheduled hours per week at 80% capacity

These standards were based on the American university working week mentioned earlier of 45 h and also recognised certain limiting factors necessary to achieve them:

Need for conversion of existing buildings
Replacement of inadequate facilities
Careful scheduling

Further research by the Californian Co-ordinating Council for Higher Education is now hoping to confirm these standards for use in the University of California and the State Colleges.

However, present utilisation figures among the individual campuses showed that in some cases room use was high while occupany was low, while in other cases the reverse was true.[3] This suggested that more flexibility for the interpretation of standards would be obtained if these two traditional components of utilisation could be combined into a single index:

Station (place) occupancy × room use = Av. no. of hours per week a single station is used,

e.g. the Master Plan recommendations would show:

60% × 30 = 18 therefore each lecture student station planned should be used on the average about 18 h per week as the Utilisation Standard.

The basic measure used in the California study for determining classroom capacity is the Weekly Student Contact Hour (WSCH). This represents the actual time a student station is occupied and can be translated to other student units based on the experience of the particular institution, e.g. Capacity in WSCH = Utilisation standard × no. of (classroom) Stations.

This can therefore be used to analyse existing situations and especially to show the effect of higher utilisation in terms of students to be accommodated.

1. Bibl. 57, p. 96.
2. This revised a standard suggested by the earlier (1955) 'Restudy' [Bibl. 56, p. 321]:

Classrooms	36 scheduled hours per week at 67%
Teaching laboratories	24 scheduled hours per week at 80%

which the Master Plan had to admit, while being theoretically possible had proved 'under current operational procedures' not to be realisable. [Bibl. 57, p. 92.]
3. Bibl. 59, p. 3, Table 1.

As an application of these utilisation standards to planning new lecture and seminar facilities the California study derives for following formula[1] relating them to room areas required:

$$\frac{\text{Assignable sq.ft/place for a room category}}{\text{Utilisation standard}} = \text{ASF/per WSCH}$$

Ex. The California Study proposed a maximum space standard of 15 assignable sq.ft per student place for lecture rooms (this was based on existing rooms which varied from 13·4 sq.ft/place at the University of California to 17·3 sq.ft/place in the Junior Colleges). If the utilisation standard is 18, then from formula:

$$\tfrac{15}{18} \times 100 = 83 \text{ assignable sq.ft per 100 weekly student contact hours.}$$

This methodology does not, however, give any further indication of the way such space for lecture use will then be broken down into room capacities to meet differing student and teaching loads. It is in this application of standards of utilisation that the planning work for the new university at Bochum, Germany, undertaken by the Institut fur Schulbau, Aachen, is of great interest.

Ruhr University of Bochum

The method of 'inscriptions' for lecture courses by students at the beginning of each semester, which has been standard procedure in German universities, allows an accurate forecast to be made of the number of students who have paid to attend any particular lecture. However, the discrepancy between these 'inscriptions' and the actual attendance figures is often high and has already been referred to.

In a method of analysis of lecture room utilisation used at T.H. Aachen a comparative chart was drawn indicating all room sizes and use for each in periods per week.[2] Into this was added the actual occupancy in terms of class size for each period and blank periods were allowed when the room was used for lecture preparation (Fig. 10*a*).

This method of demonstrating the *status quo* situation with regard to the use of the lecture rooms was then adapted to form the basis of theoretical study aimed at answering the first questions for a university redevelopment programme:

> Likely size of class and times occurring
> Main categories of lecture room size needed
> Place where lectures will be required

1   The primary step was to analyse the use of all existing lecture rooms at T.H. Aachen which could be withdrawn from direct relation to their parent departments; it was found that 50% of all classes could be considered in this way as taking place in anonymous, neutral, and not highly serviced theatres.

The graph of these class sizes against frequency was then drawn with no reference to special subjects or existing rooms. Onto this was imposed a series of steps (representing room sizes) so that all class requirements (represented by the area under the graph), lay within an appropriate room category. The imposition of these steps by width increments of 25 h represented the desired minimum level of use for the lecture rooms.

This figure of 25 h arrived at was influenced by:
(i)   Working week to be approximately 32 h
(ii) Need to achieve high occupancy; not just high room use
(iii) The number of staff available could not handle a timetable based on Wissenschaftsrates rec. of 40 h per week
(iv) Reasonable progression of room category sizes which this level would provide

1. Ibid. p. 11.   2. Bibl. 55, p. 40.

(*a*). An analysis of existing lecture rooms made by T.H. Aachen. It shows expected class size for each period of use per week. Only rooms which could be withdrawn for central timetabling.

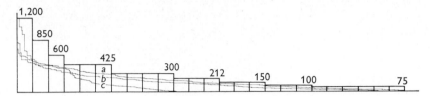

(*b*). The room use to class size requirements from T.H. Aachen survey above plotted in descending order *c*; similar curves plotted from status quo of lectures at University of Munster *a*, and University of Bonn *b*. The theoretical steps of lecture size are imposed to satisfy a 25 h per week utilisation standard.

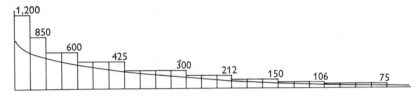

(*c*). An average curve of lecture load derived from those above and taken as the basis of central lecture room needs for the New University of Bochum.

Fig. 10. Room use in hours per week.

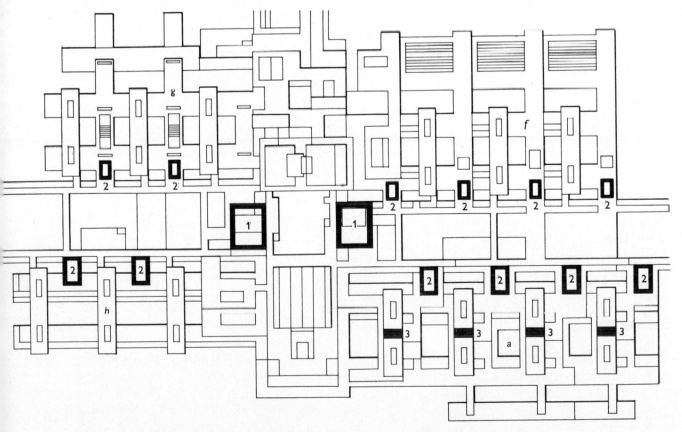

Fig. 11. Plan proposed for University of Bochum, scale 1:5000. Types of lecture-room accommodation are: 1, fully withdrawn to central lecture blocks and centrally timetabled; 2, related to departmental buildings but centrally timetabled; 3, in departmental buildings and controlled by them (Natural Sciences only).

This process had now projected a model for the theoretical needs of lecture rooms for all the 'withdrawn' lectures at T.H. Aachen. To make this theory applicable for other situations, curves of class size:frequency were drawn for two other similar size universities (Munster and Bonn) and adjusted so that all three were on the same basis (Fig. 10*b*). From this an average curve based on existing teaching patterns was projected to represent the lecture load likely for the new University of Bochum and room size categories again imposed for a 25 h use level (Fig. 10*c*). The actual detail increments of size of these steps to follow the curve was decided on by cost where changes occur in technical equipment or room form (e.g. need for sound amplification; trapezoidal plan over approx. 300).[1]

The final theoretical range of room sizes satisfying the graphical projection of class size: frequency was taken as

$$75 \quad 106 \quad 150 \quad 212 \quad 300 \quad 425 \quad 600 \quad 850 \quad 1{,}200.$$

2   With this method used as the basis for determining all the 'withdrawable' lecture theatres needed at Bochum, the next stage was to consider the requirements for the other 50 % of rooms considered as 'non-withdrawable'. These were still assumed to be centrally timetabled but having also to be related more closely to a teaching area (e.g. Medical Pathology or Inorganic Chemistry lecture rooms easily accessible to laboratories, see Fig. 11). Under these conditions it was decided that there should be small groups of rooms closely related to the buildings for Medicine and Science able to cope with:

Maximum class size likely
Use of equipment required

The sizes of rooms in these groups can be determined in a similar way to that described for 'withdrawable' rooms above by analysing the teaching pattern of lecture chairs, student numbers and course structures. It was suggested that the use of these rooms might be to a lower standard of utilisation, e.g. 20 h per week due to the need to cope with peak sizes of lectures and the need to build to this maximum size for future economy.

The increments by room capacity for these related groups of rooms would be on the range already established although sizes over 425 would be rarely needed.

3   A third category of lecture rooms was also recognised for Bochum which could not be subject to the use analysis described above. This was for rooms of under 100 places which were needed within laboratory buildings for unscheduled seminar lectures and for short periods of group instruction; it was assumed that their use would be entirely the responsibility of the department in whose building the room occurred.

c. Implications for Higher U.K. Standards

The level of use of the average science lecture room in the U.K. (1964–65) has been shown to approximate to 13·0 h out of a timetable week of 32 h. If for a typical university in the group surveyed the lecture year is 25 weeks (e.g. as at Manchester University) then lecture facilities are only being used for 325 h per year for timetabled lectures. The implication of such low levels of plant utilisation was discussed in an article on the output of universities by Professor B. R. Williams where he examined[2] the possibility of arranging two university 'years' in every 12 months and so doubling the U/G numbers. (A suggestion which would certainly make doubling of the plant use given above seem a more reasonable return for the capital cost of building.) However, in

1. Bibl. 78, pt. I.   2. Bibl. 60, p. 190.

arguing all aspects of such 'double banking' he finally concluded that the longer or four-term academic year might be 'the most promising path to reform'.

In terms of lecture-room efficiency the higher the utilisation factor (room use × occupancy) the more telling would be the potential gain of the longer year. At present the usage of 13 h per week at approximately 50% capacity gives a place utilisation factor of $6\frac{1}{2}$ (cf. California minimum recommendations of 18). If the comparable U.K. figures to be achieved were 20 h per week at 60% then a factor of 12 results, which is nearly double the existing. As found with both German and American experience the two major requirements for an increase in utilisation are:

A means of using each lecture room more often
The ability to fit class sizes to match room sizes

The potential of any such increase can be measured in a variety of ways, e.g.

Extra number of lectures possible in a given situation
Reduced number of rooms needed in new or replanned areas

An example of a proposal for savings in capital expenditure by means of careful programme analysis was recorded in the University of Leeds Development Plan 1960.[1] In it lecture-room requirements from various departments of the new Medical School totalling 34,000 sq.ft were shown to be subject to a contraction of 50% if the principle of sharing and central control were acceptable and rooms were planned on this basis.

Studies such as this, and the building of the first independent blocks of common user lecture rooms for the sciences, have indicated opportunities for making a more efficient use of lecture space. A further recognition of the need for higher utilisation is also contained in the statements of intention for new universities, e.g.:

University of Surrey	Centralised lecture rooms allocated by the University administration 'is the only practicable solution on economic grounds'[2]
University of Warwick	Average use of (science) lecture rooms will not exceed 18 h per week (this figure allows some time for setting up demonstrations between lecture periods); use for humanities to be 23 h per week[3]
University of York	25 h per week for non-science lecture rooms, 20 h per week for science ('we have allocated two free periods per day to the science lecture theatres where more time is required to assemble and dismantle apparatus'). A space occupancy factor of 75% is also shown, and the working week is taken as 30 h[4]

The Development Plan for York went on to add: 'the factors which we have assumed will represent a relatively intense use of space and will be something of a challenge to the University administration if they are to be adhered to.'

The latter room use in hours per week does in fact correspond with the assumptions already quoted for Bochum where a use of 20 h per week was suggested as the minimum for the related groups of science lecture rooms and 25 h per week for the majority of science lecture rooms 'withdrawn' from the departments.

At Bochum, as at Warwick or York, the suggested reason for the lower value for room use per week for science rooms was given as the extra needs for setting up complex demonstrations before lectures. The pattern of lectures in Germany has always

1. Bibl. 52, p. 117.
2. Programme prepared (1964) as brief for architects by University Buildings Officer.
3. Bibl. 54, p. 14.   4. Bibl. 53, p. 33.

traditionally concentrated on large and carefully prepared lecture demonstrations and an emphasis on visual presentation techniques.

For instance at T.H. Aachen, where the average use in hours per week for central rooms for Technology and Natural Science was 37 h per week, another four rooms specifically for chemistry had an average of only 11 h use per week with remainder of the time ostensibly for preparation. It was interesting to note that in this instance the planning office considered that if it had been possible to arrange for demonstrations to be moved complete into the lecture from adjacent preparation areas, this extravagant use of time could have been reduced to a quarter hour interval between lectures.

From the survey of science lecture rooms in England the following information on the existing provision for lecture demonstrations was available:

NO preparation area	Adjacent area* but NOT used	Related† preparation area	Adjacent preparation area
30/74	5/74	14/74	25/74

    * Rooms now used for other purposes.   † Along corridor on same level.

Of these rooms only 7/74 had movable trolley sections of the demonstration bench. (These were all built since 1960 and represented 1/6 of all rooms built since then).

Of the rooms with related or adjacent preparation areas 6/39 reported that no lecture demonstrations ever took place. If this figure is taken together with rooms without preparation areas (or with obsolete areas) then over 50% of all science rooms did not apparently have complex lecture demonstrations.

In rooms which were reported to have demonstrations these only amounted to between one and three periods per week on average.

The implications of these figures and other relevant evidence (see Chapter 1, Section *a*) tend to confirm the decrease in importance of the complex 'set piece' demonstration in science lectures and the corresponding increase in theoretical transfer by visual aids such as film, slides or television. When demonstrations are likely to be required (e.g. for first-year Physics) careful preplanning of new facilities, with movable sections of the demonstration bench, easy access and duplication of services to preparation areas, all mean less time needed for setting up apparatus and adjustment in the lecture room. (Where such aids already exist departments report that the majority of demonstrations can be set up in the lecture room during the change-over between classes.) This therefore helps to eliminate one of the most widely quoted, but not necessarily accurate, objections to any intensive use proposals for science lecture rooms.

Any arguments for higher utilisation such as these will necessarily need at the same time new methods of approach both from university staff and those designing university buildings, e.g.:

1   New lecture accommodation planned for maximum efficiency of use by a range of subjects will have to provide easy access to the teaching hinterland for students, staff, equipment and interlink services. This may well become an important determinant in deciding the position, size and nature of groupings required.

2   Departmental teaching laboratories will have to have teaching stations or localised lecture points to provide an opportunity for 'chance' lectures—often consisting of a whole laboratory class which needs to be shown a theoretical point. Facilities in the laboratories need to be planned at an early stage (e.g. chalkboards, projection screens well placed and provision for overhead projectors, television). The extent of large laboratories over 50 ft to 60 ft long suggests a special hier-

archy of small discussion lecture rooms for 40–80 could well be included in teaching areas (cf. at University of Bochum).

3 An average use of between 4 and 5 h a day for any one room will still leave certain opportunities for special lectures or testing of apparatus. Longer processes such as setting up complex coloured chalkboard diagrams may demand the use of more recent techniques such as the overhead projector with sets of prepared transparent foils.

4 The actual process of central timetabling and organisation for shared use will call for more administrative control by the university—especially if rooms are to be worked to a high level of use and kept under review throughout the year.

Central timetabling is not a new problem and in most universities the lecture rooms and classrooms for non-technical subjects are allocated by the central administration and not by departments. Sometimes, as has been referred to (Chapter 4, Section *a*), this central allocation is also able to take account of spare periods in science lecture rooms when they are offered by the departments concerned. If, however, the majority of science lecture rooms were to be centrally allocated as well then the process becomes more intricate. When this reaches the proportion of the shared lecture rooms at the University of Bochum (future population to be 10,000) it becomes a mathematical problem needing the aid of a computer rather than extra staff at the central registry. The initial computer-controlled program at Bochum was arranged to reconsider the timetable and make necessary amendments once every semester. It has now been considered necessary to make this control more sophisticated to allow for fluctuation in class size during the term and it is planned that the computer will go through the process of re-timetabling three times each semester.[1]

An early example of the application of the computer to university timetable construction was at Purdue University, U.S.A., in 1958 with a population of 20,000 students. Reports indicate that the use of the computer for a large-scale problem such as this is well justified. On the question of population size in relation to computer use for time-tabling, E. D. Barraclough of the University of Newcastle has written:[2] 'In Britain the main concern for the construction of timetables is within the comparatively small scale but complex problems arising in schools. British Universities are generally smaller than American ones and also tend to arrange their teaching within departments so that the problems of many thousands of students all choosing from the same course does not arise.'

The approximate comparison between average university size was:

U.S.A.	10,800 (1960)[3]
England	4,600 (1964)[4]

Of the English universities seven out of twenty-two were, however, at that time above the national average for full-time population. The recommendations of the Committee on Higher Education may easily create a need for more rapid growth in the civic universities in the 1970s.[5] This, taken together with the breakdown of departmental boundaries and the emphasis on multi-purpose accommodation (see Chapter 1, Section *b*), could at least bring these seven into the class for complex timetabling along with new universities such as Essex and Warwick where populations in the range from 10,000 to 20,000 are already planned for. As a result, planning now will have to allow for the possibility of far greater control in the use and administration of lecture facilities in the next decade.

1. In making out the timetable the computer is programmed to allow as well for maximum travel distance between lecture rooms and department within the general 'walkability' radius of 8 min for the whole university.
2. Bibl. 61, p. 136.   3. Bibl. 49, p. 4.   4. Bibl. 44, p. 12, Table 1.   5. Bibl. 3, p. 163.

If, therefore, it can be shown that the role of the lecture for the sciences is becoming more general in its presentation requirements, and less reliant on complex demonstrations and apparatus, how should the timetable levels for efficiency of use of science lecture rooms be decided. And what should be the degree of difference of use compared with lecture rooms for other subjects (cf. 1 h differential per day quoted for Sciences : Arts in new U.K. universities).

As the California authorities see it 'a standard no matter how stringent or lenient must be chosen arbitrarily'.[1] But they were at least able to rely on the weight of experience on utilisation since a previous standard had been established;[2] and they were able to modify this until it appeared both reasonable and attainable (see Chapter 4, Section *b*).

In Great Britain no standards have been generally set and tested out as the minimum criteria for utilisation of plant either amongst universities receiving Government grants or between the universities themselves.[3] Until such a testing or weight of evidence is collected no valid or scientific analysis can be made. However, certain initial assumptions could be adopted as a basis for this testing.

1   The minimum average occupancy factor of 60% for lecture and classrooms be maintained on the strength of the experience in California (cf. existing U.K. levels, Chapter 4, Section *a*).
2   A minimum use of 20 h per week for all science lecture rooms be maintained. While experience on this is gained, universities should analyse what proportion of science rooms might be satisfactorily controlled to the higher standard, e.g. 25 h per week which would be maintained for non-science subjects.

These factors would allow the proposed new university standards and their related design decisions to be consolidated to act as a basis for future experiment. The real relevance would, however, be for the various existing and well-established universities where the pressure for extra places in higher education in the 1970s is going to put the greatest demand. Rebuilding and expansion programmes for these, the majority tightly constrained 'in-town' situations with little extra land space available, must be based on principles of design closely interlinked with principles for maximum efficiency of use for all types of building.

In 1964–65 the total number of Natural Science lecture places for seven English universities surveyed was 11,800 which represented an average accommodation of 1,690 places and 11 lecture rooms per university (see Chapter 3).

The average distribution of room sizes was:

Size group	Under 100	101/200	201/300	Over 300
Frequency/7	4 1/7	4 3/7	1 6/7	1

This is able to suggest, although only in outline form, the structure of a typified university in relation to its science lecture rooms:

approx. 1,690 places : 11 rooms 4 at 100 or less
4 at 100/200
2 at 200/300
1 at 300 or more

1. Bibl. 59, p. 3.   2. Bibl. 57, p. 96.
3. A Ministry of Education Working Party recommendation to C.A.T.S. was for use of 20 h out of 30 h for lecture rooms at an 80% occupancy.

If the method of graphical analysis already described,[1] in reference to the University of Bochum (Figs. 10*a*–*c*), is applied to the available information on individual room sizes and their actual use, not only can the lecture requirement for an 'average' situation be defined (Fig. 12*a*) but, by taking a range of room sizes, the theoretical requirement in rooms to meet this lecture load is derived.

Any decision on ranges of room size must necessarily mean an arbitrary decision unless, as was shown for Bochum, the sizes themselves are decided as reflecting the *status quo* of class inscriptions. As discussed elsewhere there may, however, be far more flexibility in providing room sizes whose increments reflect increments of the teaching pattern, e.g. laboratory classes might be multiples of forty and lecture course structures would be guided by this. In addition, rooms which reflect a simple arithmetic progression give extra opportunities in fitting class to room size. As a result a case can be made for a series 80, 120, 160, 200, 240, 280, 320 for room capacities which allows not only the often occurring multiples of a 40-laboratory group to be accommodated but also provides suitable number combinations for different groups to be amalgamated for lecturing. When this range of room increments is applied to the graph of the 1963/64 *status quo* teaching load for Natural Science lectures, together with the existing use increments of 13 h per week (see Chapter 4, Section *a*) the following model emerges:

Use hours per week	Room sizes						
	320	280	240	200	160	120	80
13	1	1	—	1	2	2	4

which gives 1,680 places and 11 rooms for the 'average' university within the range sampled (Fig. 12*b*).

By establishing an 'average' situation in relation to the existing use of rooms in hours per week it is now possible to test out the variations in room and size requirements if this utilisation factor is altered (Fig. 12*c*). From amended increments for use in hours per week but from the same range of room sizes the following results may be obtained:

Utilisation factor at (hours per week)	Lecture room sizes required						
	320	280	240	200	160	120	80
10	1	1	1	1	3	3	4
15	1	1	—	1	2	2	3
20	1	—	1	—	1	2	2
25	1	—	—	1	1	1	2
30	1	—	—	1	1	1	1

In terms of comparative numbers of places and rooms this can be rearranged as:

Utilisation factor at (hours per week)	Lecture places	Number of rooms
10	2,200	14
15	1,520	10
20	1,120	7
25	960	6
30	880	5

This represents the science lecture room needs for the 'average' university (from survey 1964/65) at different theoretical levels of utilisation. It is based on the assumption that in practice shared use of rooms would be possible through central control and time-tabling and that lecture rooms would be designed to allow for this (e.g. extracted from

1. Bibl. 62, p. 10.

departments into groupings). However, even if it was viable to create a pattern of rooms timetabled to satisfy lecture loads at 30 h per week, it is useful to note that, for the total science lecturing load taken here as a basis, the gain from 25 h to 30 h per week use is only represented by a building saving of one room and eighty places. By contrast the increase in use of rooms from 10 h per week to 15 h per week provides for a saving of four rooms and 680 places. Factors such as this, which are related to the ultimate lecture and student loads, will act as a means of establishing the worth-while limits for room use.

This may be considered to be a strong confirmation for establishing the basic science room use at 20 h per week and no higher at the present time given the existing size and science teaching loads of the older English universities. To aim for much higher limits would be to create an administrative problem that may not be justified in terms of the extra savings.

As is shown also on the table an increase of use from the existing level 13 h per week to 20 h per week represents a valuable reduction in theoretical requirement from 1,680 places in 11 rooms to 1,120 places in 7 rooms.

If in time a general increase in size of universities and science populations were to alter considerably the 'average' structure taken for this exercise then a reappraisal of the gains which would return from much higher room use could be equated to extra savings either in terms of capital cost saved or possibilities for extra lecture potential. It should though be noted from the curve of requirement on the graph rising through the range of lecture sizes that the wider the use increment (i.e. the more use per week a room is put too) the greater is the gap between nominal size and nominal occupancy. As a result the actual efficiency through occupancy cannot keep pace with the extra efficiency through longer use of rooms.

The creation of a '20 h model' for an average university teaching situation as described also provides the basis for comparison with completely different lecture room/teaching patterns as suggested for several of the new universities. In the draft programme for Surrey it was proposed that no lecture room, apart from what on the Continent is termed the auditorium maximum, should exceed a capacity of 100. At York the Development Plan gives a more fully documented analysis of teaching patterns and class size and proposed that all lecture rooms should be for classes of 40 nominal at an assumed occupancy of 75 %, i.e. 30 actual users always maintained.

If for the projected 20 h per week utilisation model (Fig. 12c) it is assumed that these rooms average 50 % occupancy (comparable to present), then the total need in useful places built would be 560. To meet the same student lecture load rooms that would have to be built to the York pattern:

> 'Average' existing science lecture needs at 20 h per week = 7 rooms: 1,120 places built.
> 'York' pattern for same science teaching load at 20 h per week = 19 rooms: 760 places built.[1]

A complete change of teaching pattern and imposed class sizes such as this represent obstacles in attempting to make some general proposals for analysis. In addition:

1   Sudden growth in importance of particular teaching areas and changes in professor can affect potential class sizes. The withdrawal of rooms from 'departments' and the general tenant status of lecture room users means most of this can be taken out in the timetabling.

1. The lecture rooms programmed at York as 40 (nominal) are stated in the Development Plan to be able to hold 80 maximum. This space use can therefore be considered as equivalent to building 1,520 places.

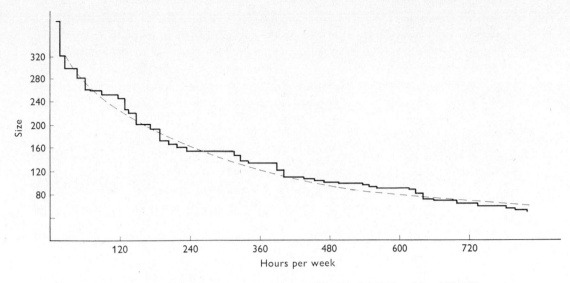

Fig. 12(*a*). Utilisation of science lecture rooms in English Universities, 1964–65.

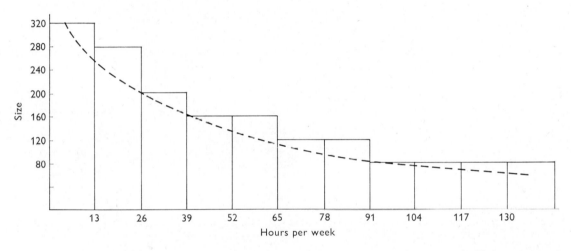

Fig. 12(*b*). A curve derived from the graph above to represent the science lecture needs of the average English University, 1964–65. Lecture-room sizes by increments of 40 imposed to satisfy existing utilisation of 13 h per week.

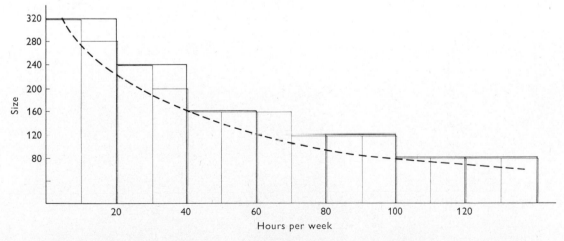

Fig. 12(*c*). The requirements for lecture-room sizes at 10 h per week and 20 h per week utilisation.

2 Any projected curve of lecture requirements, whether for a whole university or for a category of subjects, may alter during the growth of the university with changes of policy and physical conditioning elements. This must mean that rooms built will have to be selected to satisfy the requirements at a particular stage.[1] The use of mechanical/computer techniques at growth stages to assess the feedback information will help in the selection of the next sizes to be built.

For application of a methodology to total university growth and projections for use and room size it would also be important to categorise types of lecture accommodation:

1 By Subjects   Arts may have a potential for much higher use factors than pure science. The correct levels to apply for other categories, e.g. technology can only be found by careful analysis of the particular teaching pattern.

2 By Location   Of the types of lecture room referred to—centralised, related and embedded—only the latter are not suitable for central time-tabling. For centralised and related/attached rooms the travel distance between them and their student hinterlands will influence the timetable levels to be achieved.

1. At Bochum University it is only planned to build two-thirds of rooms programmed at any stage of growth to allow for errors or changes of pattern to be taken up.

5. PRINCIPLES FOR LECTURE GROUPINGS

The interaction of subjects and the general breaking down of departmental boundaries in the sciences has meant that while the science lecture room still needs to be related to its teaching hinterlands there has been an increasing need for it to serve, and be positioned to serve, students coming from a variety of different basic subjects (e.g. for cross-courses or for schools of study). In addition a series of other factors in lecture-room planning have become increasingly evident:

1 Need for higher utilisation and more efficient use of lecturing space (see Chapter 4, Section c).
2 Possibility of a more general use of the science lecture room allowing for central, i.e. non-departmental, control and timetabling (see Chapter 1, Section a).
3 The case for teaching laboratories for the sciences to be considered as areas of flexible standard space allowing for maximum change and rearrangement of users (see Chapter 2, Section b).
4 The apparent economies of grouping special non-standard lecture spaces together rather than embedding them individually in otherwise uniform science buildings (see Chapter 11).
5 A greater reliance on centralised teaching methods and aids requiring special facilities and interlinking services (see Chapter 1, Section b).

As a result a number of universities in different countries have built, or planned, centralised blocks of science lecture rooms which respond to these factors (Figs. 13a–c). Most have provided for large student concentrations of approximately 2,000 to 3,000 lecture places and in the U.S.A. a 'lecture centre' for the University of Illinois at Congress Circle is planned for both arts and sciences with over 4,000 places.[1]

The variation of room size incorporated and the capacity in student places for some typical examples of these science lecture blocks are shown on p. 50.

These blocks represent fully 'withdrawn' lecture rooms that can be administered centrally and are separated from the teaching laboratory and other science buildings. They also represent in planning terms large units of a high order of permanence, designed to meet a special set of circumstances, generating high movement loadings and, as total building units, expensive. The general categories of size indicate that they have been thought of as a single item, not to be repeated and their architectural character suggests that once completed they are not subject to alteration or extension.

Each of these lecture blocks is related to an area of teaching space which supports a known or assumed student teaching load. These have been the determining factors in deciding how many rooms are needed in such a block and what size these rooms need to be. At Manchester University, for instance, the very high number of flat-floored rooms for 80 students reflects the need for a large number of mathematics lectures. At

1. Bibl. 48, p. 29. In addition at least ten other lecture centres similar to the one at Chicago, i.e. for all subject groupings, are planned for various units of the New York State University alone. The Chicago campus is a new one with a planned enrolment of 20,000.

Leeds the requirements are built up to meet the forecast pattern of lecture sizes by the departments of Physics, Zoology, Botany, Geology and Mathematics whose buildings are all within a convenient walking distance from the block.

University	Room sizes	Total places	Gross area (s.f.)	Date of building
U.K.				
Manchester	1 at 450			
	1 at 250			
	20 at 80 (f)	2,300	64,000	1960–63*
Manchester (C.S.T.)	1 at 500			
	2 at 300			
	6 at 140			
	12 at 70 (f)	2,780	110,000	1959–62†
Leeds	2 at 250			
	1 at 200			
	2 at 150			
	4 at 100			
	16 at 75	2,650	60,000	1965 (project)‡
Brunel	3 at 180			
	3 at 100			
	8 at 70			
	4 at 60 (f)			
	8 at 40 (f)		Phase 1:	
	6 at 25 (f)	2,110	56,000	1965 (project)‡
Germany				
Bochum	1 at 850			
	1 at 600			
	1 at 425			
	2 at 300			
	1 at 212			
	1 at 150			
	1 at 106			
	2 at 75	3,093	—	1965 (project)§
Holland				
T.H. Delft	1 at 1,500‖			
	2 at 350			
	2 at 250	2,280	—	1963–65¶

(f) Flat floored; all others stepped.
* Bibl. 34, p. 201.
‡ Details from architects concerned.
‖ Auditorium maximum for general use.

† Bibl. 31, p. 281.
§ Details from architects concerned.
¶ Bibl. 32, p. 160.

A pedestrian time scale as a determining factor in planning university layouts has been an influential arbiter in many of the new university proposals. At Bochum a 'walkability' radius of 8 minutes has been taken as the maximum criterion for the distance of any laboratory to any lecture room or vice versa.[1] At York the whole of the initial plan for colleges and practical teaching areas is kept within an area of diameter of 10 minutes walking.[2] The new southwards extension of the University of Leeds towards the town centre provides for a pedestrian spine of total extent from one corner of the site to the other of 10 minutes and for the maximum separation of related departments to be approximately 7 minutes.[3] At Brunel all departments will be within 3 or 4 minutes radius of the lecture block in the centre of the development (Fig. 14b).

For existing universities on restricted sites the constraints of available area often mean that while buildings are too close to provide for future expansion they are at

1. Bibl. 55, p. 46.
2. Bibl. 53, p. 50.
3. Bibl. 52, Section 3, p. 67.

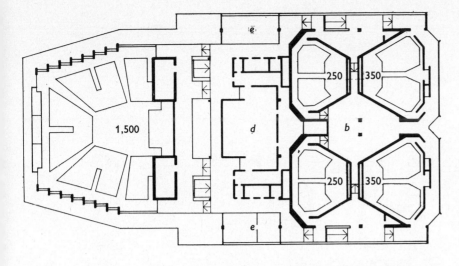

Fig. 13(*a*). The T. H. Delft central lecture block for Physics with auditorium maximum. Architects: Van den Broek and Bakema.

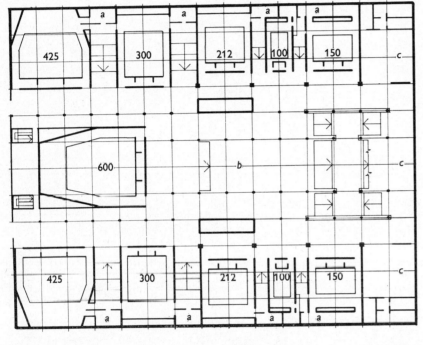

Fig. 13(*b*). University of Bochum central lecture block providing all 'withdrawn' theatres serving Sciences and Technology. Preliminary design by Hentrich and Petschnigg, 1965.

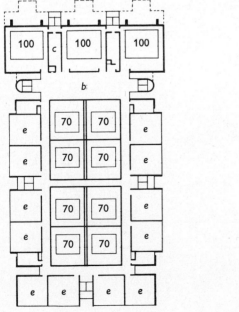

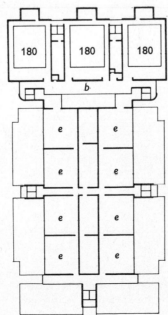

Fig. 13(*c*). Brunel University central lecture and classroom block. Preliminary design by Richard Sheppard, Robson and Partners, 1965.

a, Preparation.   *b*, Foyer.   *c*, Cloakrooms.   *d*, Senate.   *e*, Seminar.   Scale 1:1000.

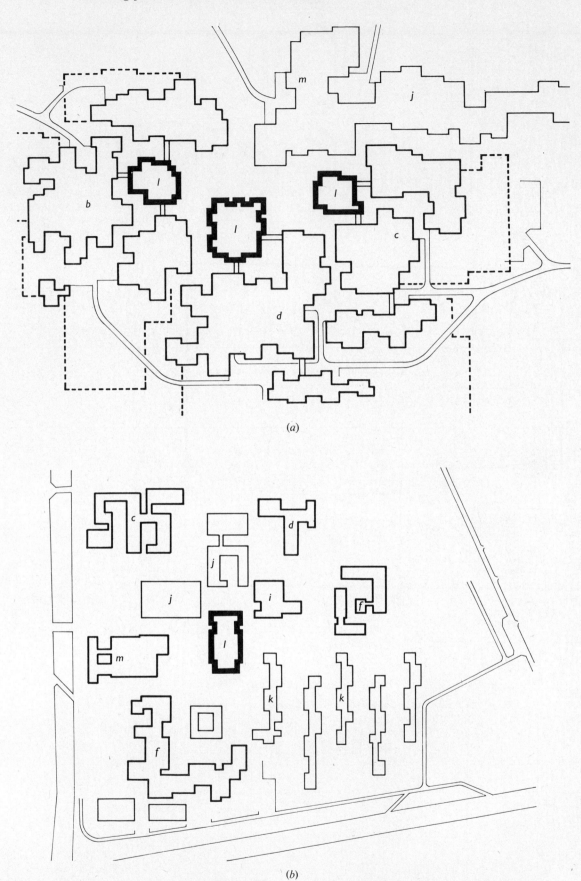

(a)

(b)

Fig. 14. Examples of two new Universities where it is planned 1965 to have central lecture blocks for Science and Technology. Scale 1:5000. (a). Marburg; (b). Brunel. [Key to building areas as Fig. 9, p. 28.]

least providing for ease of movement and interaction both for staff and students. The general extent of some existing and proposed sites are shown by the following table:

| University | Maximum travel distances between | |
	Science lecture rooms (ft)	Farthest buildings for Science and Technology (ft)
U.K.		
Birmingham	1,300	2,000
Bristol	1,200	1,200
Cambridge*	900 (2,600)†	1,400 (2,800)
Durham*	900	1,200
Manchester	1,300	1,400
Newcastle	800	1,700
Nottingham*	900	1,200
Brunel‡	central block	1,400
York‡	2,000	2,300
Germany		
Marburg‡	1,000§	2,000
Bochum‡	1,200	1,800

    * Separate science areas only.
    † With outlying Chemistry buildings.
    ‡ New development plans.
    § Distance between three central lecture blocks.

Planning for the new Brunel University at Uxbridge has demonstrated how requirements of movement and student hinterland area can interact to govern the design principles. The decision that the major bulk of all lecture rooms (80–90%) should be withdrawn to a single lecture block has meant that this will reflect the lecture load imposed by the maximum of 4,000 students planned for on the campus at any time. These 4,000 students will in turn be supported by a calculated area of gross floor space on a site which allows any building to be within easy reach of the central lecture block. In addition, not only is the lecture block centralised but also other communal acivities, e.g. refectory, administration and student union. These too are made to relate to the student population ceiling and to a basic philosophy that when this campus has reached its target figure expansion will take place by establishing a second similar configuration.

Such a pattern, which may be termed centripetal, is necessarily a finite one with given outer bounds dependent on time from the centre (Fig. 15a). A variant of this would be to have two or three groups of lecture rooms around an open centre while still maintaining the basic relationships between distance, teaching hinterland and lecture-room requirements (cf. new science area for the University of Marburg[1] (Fig. 14a)).

In this way it could be possible to examine a whole vocabulary of different topological solutions for lecture rooms in relation to teaching space or, if required, for any other centralised facility to its supporting hinterland. The linear development is an obvious alternative with a strip of 'hinterland' supporting lecture blocks at intervals each closely connected to the main student circulation route (Figs. 15b–d). The frequency of these intervals will, however, depend not only on maximum walking distances between blocks but also on the strength of the section of hinterland by area and by the lecture load which its users generate (Fig. 16).

1. Bibl. 41, p. 317.

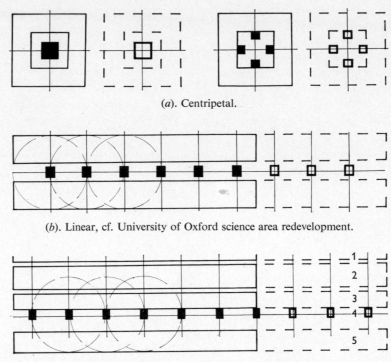

(*a*). Centripetal.

(*b*). Linear, cf. University of Oxford science area redevelopment.

(*c*). Linear. 1, Servicing; 2, Research; 3, Teaching; 4, Central facilities; 5, Residential.

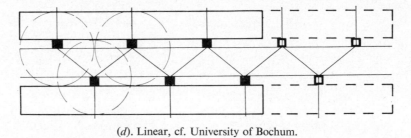

(*d*). Linear, cf. University of Bochum.

Fig. 15. The lecture grouping in relation to its supporting hinterland. Topological Studies.

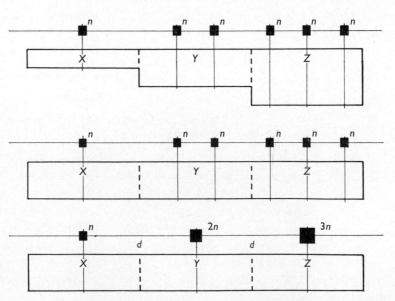

Fig. 16. The lecture group frequency and size in relation to standard lengths of supporting hinterland of different area or with different teaching loads.

The theoretical relationship between any area of teaching hinterland and the lecture rooms which it will support suggests that if these lecture rooms are gathered into 'nodal' points:

> These nodes will retain their validity even if the subject allocated to that particular hinterland changes providing it is within the same general category, e.g. the lecture space requirements of most of the Natural Science subjects per student place are approximately the same but requirements for arts:sciences are not likely to be identical.

> The expansion or contraction in importance of subjects or schools of study occupying the teaching hinterland may inevitably mean variations in requirement for individual nodes. Differences in teaching methods will also affect the composition of the nodes. This may represent a case for keeping them limited in size (and therefore greater by frequency) and designing them with a degree of inherent flexibility for alteration of room sizes and the possibility of addition (or contraction) of units of space.

In order to establish a general relationship between lecture groupings and their hinterlands it is necessary to summarise those planning factors which can be defined mathematically:

1 The amount of net floor space for lecture rooms required per unit of net hinterland space

   OR

   The number of lecture places required per unit of hinterland teaching load. (The complexity of crossover loads, variant teaching patterns, suggest that this may be a harder standard to achieve than one stemming from the experience of building areas.)

2 The extent of hinterland space in relation to its density in section. This density must be considered not only as floor space generating a lecture load but in addition as generating a particular type of load.

3 Viable limits by capacity for node size. Even if one single block were acceptable from above items the problems of building costs, staging, etc., might mean a case for breaking it down into smaller groups.

4 Maximum movement distances acceptable. This is the measurement which will control the upper limits of node frequency. It may prove of great importance with science lecture rooms to consider this distance in terms of time not only for ease of pedestrian access but also for the transport of apparatus, demonstration equipment, etc., from a laboratory to a lecture room.

As a first step in making a practical test of this methodology the existing relationship between departmental science lecture rooms and their supporting departmental space was made for a number of English universities. To achieve a fair comparison between the various lecture rooms, all designed at different times by different architects, a standard allocation of space per place was made for the total places per subject; this was based not on the allowable U.G.C. figures but from a separate survey showing the actual area of lecture rooms as built. (See Table on p. 56.)

A slight tendency for variation between subjects can be seen; however, the close general clustering confirms that these factors all belong to a single teaching category. Comparable Surveys for Arts and Social Sciences might be expected to show a quite different factor for lecture:departmental space due to the absence of laboratories and technical accommodation.

University	Department	Lecture places (1965)	Lecture room area*	Total departmental area (s.f. net)†	(F) $\dfrac{\text{Lecture area}}{\text{Departmental area}}$
Birmingham	Biology	184	1,840	88,614	0·021
	Chem.	835	8,350	116,251	0·072
	Physics	877	8,770	95,380	0·092
Durham	Chem. ⎱ Geol. ⎰	530	5,300	{ 56,000 { 30,000	0·062
	Physics	302	3,020	51,000	0·059
Newcastle	Physics	560‡	5,600	81,600	0·069
	Chem.	540	5,400	65,700	0·082
	Geol.	174	1,740	19,500	0·089
	Bot./Zool.	270	2,700	35,775	0·076
Nottingham	Physics	920	9,200	109,640	0·084
	Biology	360	3,600	63,240	0·057
	Chem.	658	6,580	120,000	0·055
Manchester	Chem.	550	5,500	109,000	0·051
	Physics§	750	7,500	110,000	0·068
Cambridge	Physics	928	9,280	101,000‖	0·092
	Chem.	960	9,600	149,000‖	0·064
	Bot./Zool.	475	4,750	60,000‖	0·079
				Average	0·069

* Allowance 10 s.f./place (see Chapter 7).
† Areas reported by universities for survey.   ‡ Without conference hall.
§ New building u/c; existing accommodation not included.
‖ 5/8 gross figures Cambridge University Reporter 8.12.65, p. 603.

Method

Taking the factor (F) of 0·07 as the existing standard required for science lecture rooms, if it is assumed that all these rooms can be withdrawn to act as nodes then for every X square foot of net total accommodation required to meet a particular teaching programme: Lecture-room area = 0·07X sq.ft.

If an average figure of space per lecture place is taken (S), then the number of lecture places needed (N) is:

$$N = \frac{0\cdot07X}{S} \quad \text{or, in general terms,} \quad = \frac{FX}{S}.$$

This number of places can then be related to a hinterland of x sq.ft. As

> one group of rooms
> more than one group
> individual rooms

To establish the frequency of more than one group of rooms assume capacity of places in any group is (n) places. Therefore number of groups is

$$\frac{N}{n} = \frac{\text{total places}}{\text{group capacity}},$$

and for any nodal group its hinterland

$$x_n = \frac{SN}{F}.$$

The linear relationship between a node and the hinterland is established by considering the area x_n in terms of its building form—at its simplest a linear block—as of sectional area (W) per unit run and of linear distance (D). Thus $x_n = DW$ and therefore from above

$$DW = \frac{SN}{F} \quad \text{or} \quad D = \frac{SN}{FW}.$$

From this the supporting distance D^1 can either be made to represent the node frequency or can be generated from it and the required building density established.

By this method it is also possible to test out the effect of varying certain conditions, e.g. if maximum node capacity is reduced so is the extent of the supporting hinterland (D), therefore either the frequency of the blocks is increased or the sectional density of the hinterland must be reduced to maintain a continuous development. Equally it would also be possible to take a given situation of hinterland and node size and by altering the factor (F) compare the physical implications of different teaching categories.

Examples of the methodology applied to specific situations:

Example 1

From universities survey the 'average' group of science lecture theatres was

1 at 320	2 at 160
1 at 280	2 at 120
1 at 200	4 at 80

This gives 1,680 places at existing space standards of approximately 10·0 sq.ft lecture-room space per place. According to the above calculations this should represent 0·07 of an 'average' science hinterland, therefore

$$\frac{0·07\,x}{10·0} = 1,680, \quad \text{therefore} \quad x = 240,000 \text{ sq.ft net.}$$

However, the basis of these figures and the extraction of the lecture-room factor was related to the existing use of 13·0 h per week. As has been seen from a previous study if this usage is raised to 20·0 h per week the requirement is only for 1,120 places.

Therefore for the same hinterland:

$$\frac{F \times 240,000}{10·0} = 1,120, \quad \text{therefore} \quad F = 0·05.$$

Example 2

The draft programme for a new University includes a proposal for 420,000 sq.ft (gross) of science space and it is suggested that no lecture theatres will be needed larger than 100 to 120 in capacity.

The 420,000 sq.ft of gross space = 160% of net to U.G.C. standards.
Lecture theatres at 100 places = 11·9 sq.ft net to U.G.C. standards.

If a lecture room factor of 0·06 is assumed (interpolated with that derived in Example 1) then for $x = SN/F$

$$\frac{100}{160} \times 420,000 = \frac{11·9 \times N}{0·06}, \quad \text{therefore} \quad N = 1,320.$$

Therefore there would need to be fourteen lecture rooms at approximately 100 places either in one group or broken down into two or more smaller groupings. To assess the need for the number of groups it would be necessary to analyse the science building form. If, for example, the hinterland were represented by a continuous development with an average (net) area of 225 sq.ft per ft run then for

$$D = \frac{SN}{FW}, \quad D = \frac{11·9 \times 1,320}{0·06 \times 225}, \quad \text{therefore} \quad D = 1,160 \text{ ft.}$$

If the hinterland was 1,160 ft long then for a placing of two groups representing optimum ease of access (D/4, *n*. D/2, *n*. D/4) the node frequency would be 580 ft.

1. In practice this linear distance D would have to be corrected for the insertion of other items, e.g. space for ways through building areas.

Example 3

The layout of a science area is redeveloped around a central pedestrian spine. The net floor space averages 450 sq.ft per unit run of the development. To establish the frequency of lecture nodes if they are not to exceed 400 places each (assumptions as Example 2).

$$D = \frac{SN}{FW}, \quad D = \frac{11{\cdot}9 \times 400}{0{\cdot}06 \times 450}, \quad \text{therefore} \quad D = 176 \text{ ft.}$$

These small lecture groups represent an almost continuous development at 176 ft frequency in the middle of a high-density building complex. If the lecture:hinterland factor was raised to 0·05 (see Example 1) frequency drops for same group size to 210 ft so relating location of lecture rooms to likely utilisation level.

III

DESIGN OF THE
SCIENCE LECTURE ROOM

6. ROOM FORM

a. For the Presentation of Information

The science lecture room has so far been considered as a constituent element within an overall plan and principles have been suggested for the amalgamation of these elements into groups or nodal points. In order to examine further the requirements and standards of space allocation for such groups the determinants of the design of the lecture room itself must be summarised.

These may be termed:

Presentation Criteria

and will provide conditions satisfactory for the transfer of information to a class from:

    (i) The lecturer as orator and commentator
   (ii) Apparatus and experiments set up in the demonstration area
  (iii) Images and material displayed on the visual aids wall
  (iv) Other audio-visual aids

The physical requirements of many of these criteria form some of the best documented aspects of lecture-room planning. From the Greek amphitheatre with its understanding of what can be termed 'phonics' to the nineteenth-century books on acoustics in buildings with detailed information on the setting up of a mathematical relationship between seats for equal hearing,[1] the design for the orator has received constant attention. By the late nineteenth century the rapid growth of science teaching meant that the viewing of complex apparatus and demonstrations during lectures was also the subject of analysis and rooms were designed with this as a primary factor. During the first half of the twentieth century the production of sophisticated and widely available methods of slide and film projection has meant a change of emphasis and rapid de-development in the requirements for lecture presentation. This continuing evolution of a particular room type has now been given further impetus by the use and acceptance of television in teaching.

   (i) *The lecturer as orator and commentator.* The lecturer must be able to be seen by all members of the class and if this condition is satisfied then the lines of sight mean also direct sound paths for his voice.

To achieve these sight/sound paths either the lecturer is sufficiently elevated by dais or platform or the section of the lecture theatre is stepped to provide for an unobstructed view.[2] To achieve the characteristic stepped section it is set out so that lines of sight from the object to be viewed to the viewer always clear the row in front by 4–5 in.;[3] theoretically this 'isacoustic' curve is a smooth parabola but, due to the extra complexities of constructing every row of stepping differently and allowing for intermediate treads at the gangways, a compromise of two or three different sections of constant rake is often used to approximate to the theoretical line. A straight rake can provide satisfactory views if the experimental table is not considered of primary importance.

The maximum unaided throw for a speaker's voice is 50 ft to the front and within an arc of 140°.[4] In practice this will mean that rectangular lecture rooms over approxi-

1. Bibl. 66, p. 42.   2. Bibl. 84, p. 137.   3. Bibl. 70, Sheet 1274.   4. Bibl. 80, p. 69.

mately 350 in capacity will require special reflecting forms for the ceiling and walls and the position of the speaker becomes critical. It is, therefore, at this stage that it becomes economic to have a trapezoidal plan form for the lecture room.[1] Rectangular rooms in the size range 150 to 350 will, however, give satisfactory conditions if the volume is kept low and some use made of reflected sound from the speaker's area to throw the voice to the back of the room. Over 350 capacity sound amplification will be likely to be needed and this will become mandatory for capacities of 450 and over.[2]

The axis of viewing from the lecturer to the centre of the class should be kept as horizontal as possible to avoid undue strain for the lecturer and the construction of very steep rakes, aimed at providing a view down on to the lecturing area, should therefore be avoided.

(ii) *Apparatus and experiments set up in the demonstration area*. Sight lines to the top of the demonstration bench should be possible for all members of the class. For setting out purposes this point is often taken at +3 ft 6 in. above floor or dais level. Too great an angle of view to an experiment should be avoided and the area for use should maintain in plan a 40° edge angle with the seating.[3] With movable trolley sections usually 6 ft 0 in. long these will need to 'plug' in to a permanent console or section housing the service connections; this console should allow for uninterrupted display space in the best area for viewing.

The majority of science lectures will require a frontal/oblique view, rather than a view down as for medical or anatomy lectures, and too steep a rake will give bad lines of sight to apparatus.[4] Sufficient space should be left between the position of demonstration bench and the front row for class to look at examples and move past after lectures.

(iii) *Images and material displayed on the visual aids wall*. The range of these aids will be primarily cine, slide and overhead projected images together with explanatory charts and maps. The established method for defining maximum amd minimum limits for viewing an image of width W is as multiples of that width.[5] The optimum conditions are in the region 2W to 5W with the area of best seats centred on 3·5W.[6] Maximum acceptable distance to the farthest eye is 6W from the screen, although limits of up to 7W may be tolerated. For distance to the nearest eye standards proposed have varied from 2W down to 0·87W.[7] While this latter figure is satisfactory in theory (e.g. for cinema screens for an image subtending 60° maximum to the eye) in practice it is unrealisable for lecture theatres up to 400 seats where there are requirements for lecture bench and circulation space at front. Decisions on this minimum criteria will need to consider also maximum oblique angle of view to screen (usually 40° maximum), need for more than one image to be viewed and space required for overhead projectors to be permanently installed.

In plan if the area defining the viewing limits is taken about a normal to the centreline of the image the horizontal viewing angles are:[8]

> 60° optimum,   90° acceptable,   120° maximum limit.

The use of an overhead projector is becoming widely accepted as an addition to, and possible replacement for, the blackboard.[9] It is an advantage if it can be built into the demonstration bench or, perhaps much preferable, trolley mounted to fit into a flexible assemblage of console and demonstration trolleys. (There is a case for pro-

1. Studies at the Institut fur Schulbau, Aachen by Professor Eller have shown that the trapezoidal planform is required over capacities of 400 but below that the rectangular plan can be both viable and more economic.
2. Bibl. 76, pp. 15–17.   3. Bibl. 78, pt. I, p. 5.   4. Bibl. 84, p. 136.
5. Bibl. 75, pt. II, p. 15.   6. Bibl. 78, Dwg. I.   7. Bibl. 70, Sheet 1369.
8. Bibl. 76, p. 34.   9. Bibl. 10, p. 53.

viding two overhead projectors and screen in parallel to allow students to catch up with notetaking while lecturer uses other machine.) The writing area should be at $+28$ in. so that lecturer can be seated and the lens needs to be at $1·25W$ from the screen for the widest angle types ($f = 12\frac{1}{2}$ in.).[1] The screen for an overhead projector needs to be tilted forward up to $20°$ to prevent undue keystoning and provision for this must be made at design stage of the visual aids wall.

Ideally the lower edge of any screen or area for projection should be at $+6$ ft or above in order not to dazzle the lecturer. In relation to the screen the slide or film projector should be normal to its centreline; in practice a deviation of $\pm 5°$ is quite acceptable[2] and there is always the possibility of a tilted screen wall to suit a particular projector position.

For a maximum distance to the screen of $6W$ the limit of resolving power of the eye is $0·002W$ and the smallest recognisable detail formed by projection and demonstration equipment (i.e. lettering) must be larger than $0·02W$.[3] (This would approximate to 1 in. lettering seen from 32 ft away.)

The need to design for double or triple comparison images is now becoming standard practice. At its simplest a clear expanse of white wall right across the top of the chalk-boards allows for combinations of slides and film and, if heights are adjusted, for over-head projection as well. Better edge angle conditions are obtained if the two outer screens are inclined in plan by approximately $10°$ and a much larger proportion of seats obtain satisfactory viewing;[4] a more sophisticated variant of this is to construct a long gently curving wall of radius $3·5W$ which overcomes any overlap problems where the outer screens change in plane.

(iv) *Other audio-visual aids.* Television has been limited so far in presentation alternatives to viewing by monitor (maximum 27 in. screen) or by screen projection from back of lecture theatre or rear of visual aids wall.[5]

Conditions for monitor viewing:[6]

Minimum distance	$= 4W$
Maximum distance	$= 12W$
Horizontal viewing	$= 80°$
Angle to lower edge of screen	$= 15°$

For projected television screen: Maximum distance $= 12W$

As will be seen the maximum viewing distance possible for a 27 in. monitor television will be 27 ft which is much shorter than most lecture rooms and will call for a second row of monitors to be installed half-way back, either hung from the ceiling or placed on wall brackets. A back projection television system needs a translucent section in the screen wall and a special projection room behind. (This applies also to rear projection of films and slides.) Television projected from the rear of the lecture theatre needs a projection box or separate projection area.

These basic planning requirements for presentation must necessarily be supported by satisfactory environmental and comfort conditions. They may be termed:

Support criteria

Their detailed investigation and evaluation goes beyond the scope of planning analysis into the area of building science and environmental physics. At present there is a considerable lack of agreement on standards and methods for all aspects of environ-

1. Bibl. 72, Section 3, p. 11.   2. Bibl. 71.   3. Bibl. 78, pt. I, p. 5.   4. Bibl. 75, Section 3.
5. Mr A. M. P. Brookes of the Department of Engineering, Cambridge, has pointed out that for the future the electro luminescent screen which can be hung on the visual aids wall is technically feasible and should be inexpensive compared with other systems of large scale television. It would not require back projection apparatus or video tubes and only lack of commercial pressure appears to be hindering its development.
6. Bibl. 75, pt. II, p. 19.

mental design and this is especially so as the need for more basic research work is being recognised and is developing. To provide a background to the design analysis used in this study the most important categories and considerations can be listed as:

(i) *Lighting*. While the window has traditionally been both the source for light and ventilation for lecture rooms the possibility of providing an entirely satisfactory artificial environment has now rendered its use of doubtful value.[1] Not only does it provide points of thermal and acoustic weakness together with problems of glare, direct sunlight, or visual distraction, but also the percentage of the year in which daylight on its own can act as a sole lighting medium is limited. Only by toplighting can the I.E.S. standard of 30 lm/sq.ft be achieved by daylight alone in the U.K. for a reasonable 70 to 80% of the working year (9 a.m. to 5.30 p.m.)[2] and even then a total artificial lighting system will also be required. However, if toplighting is used virtually all amenity value (i.e. for a view out) is lost and it may well be equally satisfactory to effect an equivalent lighting distribution by artificial means. This latter has the advantage that lecture rooms can then be considered as 'stackable' for multi-storey blocks.

For windowless lecture halls the artificial lighting system must be built in or designed to avoid glare, disturbing reflections or shadowing. This can be of fluorescent or tungsten or a combination of both to provide illumination to IES standard[3] for:

Writing desks,   Demonstration area,

Chalkboards,   Circulation.

A system of dimming or switching off banks of lights is also needed to provide a degree of illumination for notetaking during film or slide presentation. Any artificial lighting system needs access to it for maintenance and relamping and this, together with the possibility of adjustment and change after installation, must be considered at the design stage.

(ii) *Acoustics*. Distance of speaker to farthest part of audience will dictate the design for reflective surfaces and the design of internal elements to aid sound paths. The design of lecture rooms to a non-rectangular planform, corresponding to the traditional 'fan' shape of radiating sight and sound lines from a focus of speaker or screen, is likely to be economically viable for capacities of more than 350 to 400 seats.[4]

Acoustical conditions must be satisfactory even when the lecture room is half empty and design must avoid long sound paths, focusing shapes or flutter echo conditions. The room volume must be calculated to give a satisfactory reverberation time; and this must be related to volume per place required for efficient mechanical ventilation.[5] The lowest limits for this volume should vary in the range 90 to 160 cu.ft per place from small halls to large.[6]

(iii) *Sound reinforcement*. Will be useful for:

Reinforcing speaker's voice in large theatres

Relaying sound from other rooms and from film sound tracks

Playing tape recordings, assisting demonstrations or television presentation

It can be considered a necessary facility for most lecture theatres.

1. A survey by D. Holister for the G.L.C. (1965) has shown that over half of all instances of windowless buildings reported from 34 colleges and universities in the U.K. were in the category 'lecture room'. The survey of 80 science lecture rooms in this report showed that 22/80 had been built as windowless; of these all were completed after 1960.
2. Information from Dr D. Croghan of the Cambridge Daylighting Research Unit.   3. Bibl. 79.
4. It should be noted, however, that the 'fan' shape is not proven as an ideal answer and has not been questioned sufficiently. While giving a good theoretical solution for screen image viewing (as in a cinema) it has for a lecture situation the obvious disadvantage that the majority of seats are furthest from the lecturer.
5. Bibl. 73, p. 1563.   6. Bibl. 76, p. 17.

(iv) *Sound insulation.* The need to avoid transfer of sound from one lecture room to another applies particularly when one is over another and clapping or stamping can become noticeable. Construction must also insulate a lecture from sounds in related areas, e.g.   Foyers, circulation;   Prep. room, workshop;   Plant space

The need to prevent noise from outside such as building work, traffic or aircraft, becomes more important the larger the size of hall when an effort is being made to use the speaker's voice to the maximum. All openings, and in particular windows, represent weak points in a system of sound insulation.

(v) *Heating and ventilation.*

Ventilation methods	Natural via windows or openings
	Natural plus mechanical boost
	Natural plus separate mechanical input
	Mechanical only, with or without cooling
Heat transfer	Background system
	Separate booster units
	In conjunction with ventilation system
Cooling	Elementary system, e.g. water spray
	Full cooling plant for air conditioning

Natural ventilation via windows with a form of central heating or localised heat output gives savings of space and cost but there is no possibility of cooling and little control of conditions. It requires comparatively large openings in walls or ceilings.

Mechanical plant gives	Complete control of environment
	Quick response to conditions
	Possibility of change after installation
But	Additional plant and duct space
	Sound insulation problems

The use of mechanical plant means that a room can be used to its maximum occupancy and the conditions maintained at an optimum level for those in the lecture. The greater use that is made of lecture rooms in the summer season (traditionally vacation) the stronger the case for a cooling system, or space for it, to be included at the initial design stage.

b. Existing Designs Surveyed

The survey of 80 lecture rooms for the Natural Sciences in English universities during 1965 showed the following existing provision for teaching aids:

Chalkboards (Figs. 17*a–c*)	Fixed	30%
(primary use)	Roller	24%
	Sliding	46%
Projection screens	Diagonal	39%
	Roller	38%
	Framed/fixed	29%
	Painted wall	13%
Overhead projector		9%
Projection booth for cine film		20%
Equipment for television (Figs. 19*a–c*)		15%

The use of the diagonal screen for a short projection throw from the area of the first two or three rows was very noticeable and reflected a general need for the lecturer to show just a few slides during a lecture (Fig. 18). By having the projector near to him not only could he fit this into the flow of the lecture quite smoothly but no projectionist was needed up at the back of the room. In one particular Physics theatre (not in the survey figures) the department had a homemade version of the overhead writing projector to take slides and had tried unsuccessfully to interest manufacturers in the project.

In only 15 % of rooms would it have been possible to show comparison slides with the existing design of the visual aids wall and all of these had been built or converted since 1960 (Figs. 21 *a–e*). In most other rooms all available wall space was either:

Taken up by blackboards

Broken up by various elements

The lack of co-ordination of design of the visual aids wall was particularly noticeable in the majority of lecture theatres seen and to a great degree inhibited the amount that could be displayed (Figs. 20*a*, *b*).

Although the use of the overhead projector is at present limited, most science departmental staff showed considerable interest in its future use. (The Committee on Audio Visual Aids reported its use by only 3 % of institutions or departments questioned but referred to it as 'in many respects more flexible than the chalkboard' and recommended that it should be standard lecture theatre equipment built in whenever possible.)[1]

At present most theatres where it was wished to use the overhead projector would need either:

alteration to lecture bench area to provide sufficient space;

OR   extra provision for screen area in relation to selected projector position.

In some theatres where it is being used a convenient area of white painted wall has been found satisfactory although not overcoming any 'keystoning' effect which would be possible with a screen designed to tilt forward.

Demonstration work and experiments were assisted by bench trolley sections in seven out of 74 rooms and these, all for Chemistry or Physics use, were built since 1960 (Fig. 22*b*, *c*). The provision of services in the demonstration bench:

Service	None	1	2	3	4 +
Occurrence	10	6	8	15	35

Only rooms for Chemistry and Physics use had four or more services (Fig. 22*a*) and the greater proportion of rooms without services were in use for Botany and Zoology.

A sample survey of academic staff in the Natural Science departments at the University of Cambridge gave an indication of what services are thought to be needed for demonstration work (as opposed to any existing provision) and reflects comment from many sources on the general decline in complex lecture experiments:

	Zool.	Phys. Chem.	Physics	Bio. Chem.	Chem.	Geol.	Bot.
Gas	A	B	A	C	B	*	C
Water: bench taps	*	*	*	*	*	*	*
pipe connection	B	B	A	C	B	*	B
sink	*	*	*	*	*	*	C
Electricity: a.c. 13 amp	A	A	A	A	B	*	A
complex	*	*	B	*	*	*	*
Compressed air	*	C	*	*	*	*	*

A, often; B, sometimes; C, rare; *, not needed.

1. Bibl. 10, p. 53.

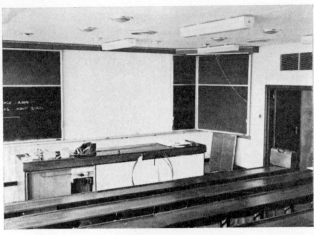

(*a*). Birmingham, Zoology (96).

(*b*). Newcastle, Mathematics (45).

(*c*). Nottingham, Chemistry (244).

Fig. 17. The use of different forms of chalkboard. Also at Newcastle the overhead writing projector with tilted screen.

Fig. 18. Many lecture theatres have diagonal projection screens to allow slides to be shown from a position near to the lecturer. Bristol, Physics (150).

(*a*). Delft, Physics. Screens linked to laboratories.

(*b*). Cambridge, Engineering. Showing originating camera on tripod with lecturer's monitor screen.

(*c*). Cambridge, Physiology. Use of remote control camera ceiling mounted over demonstrated area.

Fig. 19. The existing use of television in lecture rooms. Presentation by means of large monitor screens placed around room. Only in the larger rooms, e.g. Cambridge Engineering above, is it viable to plan for future use of expensive projection TV systems from a special projection room. Both these forms of presentation may be rendered obsolete by the development of electro luminescent television screens which could be hung directly on the front wall of a lecture theatre and which would require no projection box or tube.

Fig. 20(*a*). Birmingham, Physics (90). An example of the older theatre not originally designed for the organised use of teaching aids.

Fig. 20(*b*). Newcastle, Chemistry (130). Design solution not allowing for the simultaneous use of slides and chalkboard—a basic requirement for most Science lecture rooms.

(*a*). Bristol, Chemistry (97). Visual aids wall designed for triple comparison images with wing panels angled in plan.

(*b*). Cambridge, Physics (320). Fixed chalkboard with painted projection wall above.

(*c*). Delft, Physics (350). Vertical sliding chalkboards can be dropped down to floor.

(*d*). Manchester, Science (480). Vertical sliding chalkboards in horizontally sliding frames.

(*e*). Manchester, Science (480). Detail.

Fig. 21. Designs providing for maximum flexibility in use of projected images and chalkboard.

These priorities suggested that the requirements of the basic science lecture room could be met by:

(i)   Gas—a limited number of supply points
(ii) Tap connections—with small overflow drain
(iii) Electricity a.c. 13 amps—plenty of points
(iv) Provision of space for special requirements—perhaps by flexible lead. (Main user Physics)

The frequency of demonstrations given was difficult to assess accurately due to fluctuations by subjects during any year and the differing approach of various lecturers. The most commonly recorded frequency where demonstrations took place was 2 to 3 h a week per theatre and a maximum of five lectures with demonstrations in a week. These lectures with demonstrations were usually put on for first- or preliminary-year students. Where rooms had bench/trolley sections a whole free period in the lecture room beforehand for setting up demonstrations was not thought necessary and in most cases the apparatus could be wheeled in during a ten min changeover period.

Only 10% of lecture rooms in the survey were flat-floored and they were all for capacities under 150. The remainder were stepped in section and one room (for 165) had a ramped floor. Stepped sections were:

27% parabolic rake (or approximating to this)
73% straight rake

Of those with approximately straight, i.e. uniform, rake the size of stepping was:

Size	Up to 4 in.	4 to 8 in.	8 to 12 in.	12 to 16 in.	16 in. +
Occurrence	4	23	8	7	3

The dimensions of rooms from visual aids wall to demonstration bench to back row indicate the amount of space available to the lecturer, the steepness of the rake (Fig. 24a) and the approximate distances maximum and minimum for viewing screen images. (Figures are for equal survey sample in each capacity grouping.)

	Average science lecture-room dimensions			
Room capacity	61/100	101/140	141/180	181/260
Average no. of rows*	8·1	8·6	10·1	11·1
Space from visual aids wall to front row	10 ft 9 in.	11 ft 4 in.	11 ft 9 in.	12 ft 11 in.
Visual aids wall to centreline of bench	5 ft 0 in.	6 ft 3 in.	6 ft 3 in.	6 ft 8 in.
Centreline of bench to front row	5 ft 9 in.	5 ft 1 in.	5 ft 6 in.	6 ft 3 in.
Average steppings	6½ in.	7 in.	9 in.	10½ in.

* Widths usually 2 ft 9 in. to 2 ft 10 in.

The maximum and minimum extremes for demonstration area dimensions were:

	Room capacity	Wall to centreline of bench	Centreline of bench to front row	Subject
Maximum	250	12 ft 0 in.	9 ft 0 in.	Physics
Minimum	90	4 ft 0 in.	3 ft 3 in.	Chemistry

The minimum situation, and two others similar, were reported by staff to be unsatisfactory for reasonable lecturing.

If the distance from the farthest eye on the centreline of the lecture-room section is

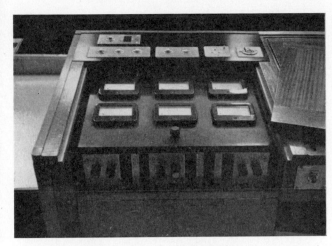

Fig. 22(a). Manchester, Science (250). Services to meet general purpose science requirements built into lecture bench.

Fig. 22(b). Nottingham, Chemistry (244). Fixed service console with movable trolley sections.

Fig. 22(c). Cambridge, Physics (320). Movable trolley section in adjacent preparation room showing flexible lead to connect to complex services in console.

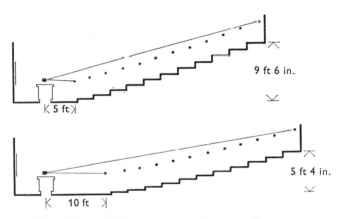

(a). Effect of increasing front space in relation to rake necessary to achieve acceptable sight lines, from Palmer and Rice.

Fig. 23. Manchester, Chemistry (150). Example of view down on to demonstration area if rake is steep.

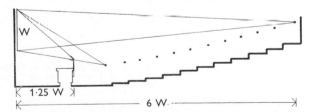

(b). Requirements for space for overhead writing projector with $12\frac{1}{2}$ in. lens.

Fig. 24. Space at front of lecture room.

taken as 6W and a theoretical size for W (screen size) assumed it is possible to analyse the existing front seat positions in terms of W.

Distance to nearest eye W	1·5 to 2*	2 to 2·5	2·5 to 3	3+
Occurrences	11	27	18	4

* 1·6 minimum recorded.

These figures represent the average existing situations and should be compared with the figure of 2W usually accepted as a reasonable lower limit and 1·4W[1] giving a minimum acceptable situation for screen to nearest place and including demonstration bench and area.

The requirement for a screen image size (theoretical) in the rooms seen was:

W in ft.	4 ft	4 ft to 5 ft	5 ft to 6 ft	6 ft to 7 ft	7 ft to 8 ft	8 ft to 9 ft.	9 ft +
Occurrences	4	7	13	17	11	4	4

From the same theoretical analysis of acceptable image size W, if it were required to install an overhead writing projector in the existing demonstration bench of science lecture theatres (Fig. 24*b*):

15 % of benches could accept overhead projectors with 14 in. lens (1·5W);[2]
37 % of benches could accept overhead projectors with 12½ in. lens (1·25W).

In the remainder of situations the position of the projector would need to be nearer to the class than the front edge of the demonstration bench for an acceptable projected image size.

Although outside the actual rooms surveyed, a further and similar use of teaching aids was on several occasions noted. This was in the related science teaching laboratories where it was necessary to give occasional short lectures on theoretical points or to demonstrate a technique of handling materials and apparatus. In these cases of 'chance' lectures there was no justification for the whole class going to a main lecture room and, for demonstrating technique, it was preferable for the students to be near their work. Design for this lecture function varied from a simple chalkboard or white-board, on which to analyse diagrams, to stepped laboratories viewing down to a demonstration bench or the length of the laboratory equipped with television screens to watch the lecturer manipulate complex apparatus (Figs. 25*a–e*).

In most cases this type of lecture has been very simply catered for as an afterthought or adaptation; only in the case of the stepped rooms had it been a primary design decision. As most laboratories can be 40 to 60 ft long the position for such a lecture 'station' needs to be specially designed perhaps with a dais, flexible provision for chalkboard and screens, facilities for projecting slides, and wired for a television camera to the demonstration bench. Visibility and audibility would be principal criteria.

Such a lecturing station if manufactured to a fairly full specification could have relevance to most of the laboratories seen and particularly to the newer ones; as a standardised item it could be inserted into laboratory buildings as needed in a similar way to a service core. In this context it was interesting to note (as mentioned in Chapter 4, Section *b*) that for the Science buildings at the new University of Bochum in order to meet the need for 'chance' discussion periods, a 75- to 80-seat lecture theatre has been made standard provision for every laboratory floor and left under the control of departments (Fig. 25*f*).

1. Bibl. 78, pt. I, p. 4.   2. Bibl. 72, p. 61.

(*a*). Newcastle. Micro anatomy laboratory with stepped floor, demonstration bench and visual aids equipment, 61 places with 11 at side benches.

(*b*). Newcastle. Anatomy lecture room equipped with TV and working surfaces. In fact acting as a form of teaching laboratory, 80 places.

(*c*). Newcastle. Provision for chalkboard and projection screen in Geology laboratory.

(*d*). Durham. Lectern, chalkboards and projector stand in Zoology laboratory

(*e*). Birmingham. Teaching station in Biochemistry laboratory with demonstration bench on dais for better visibility to back of class of 40.

(*f*). Bochum. Planning of laboratory blocks with vertical core *a*, of small lecture rooms for chance lectures in addition to usual service and circulation cores. Size of each 75 to 80. Scale 1:1000.

Fig. 25. Provision of lecturing facilities in science laboratories.

7. SPACE STANDARDS FOR ROOMS AND RELATED AREAS

The Lecture Room

Within the lecture room or theatre[1] for arts and science use in the U.K. the University Grants Committee allows net floor space as follows:[2]

first 30 students at 15 sq.ft/place
next 20 students at 12 sq.ft/place
remainder at   10 sq.ft/place

and the larger the lecture room therefore the nearer the space per place within the room approaches 10 sq.ft (Fig. 26*b*):

30 places	450 sq.ft	at 15 sq.ft/place
50 places	690 sq.ft	at 13·8 sq.ft/place
80 places	990 sq.ft	at 12·4 sq.ft/place
160 places	1,790 sq.ft	at 11·2 sq.ft/place
240 places	2,590 sq.ft	at 10·8 sq.ft/place
320 places	3,390 sq.ft	at 10·6 sq.ft/place

Comparable standards for space allocation are used in other countries.

In Germany the Wissenschaftsrates allow for lecture rooms:[3]

Less than 100 places: 0·9 sq.m/place (9·6 sq.ft)
More than 100 places: 0·8 sq.m/place (8·6 sq.ft)
Plus area for demonstrations if for science use: 0·2 sq.m/place (2·2 sq.ft)

This gives a standard allocation for all science lecture capacities over 100 of a nominal 10·8 sq.ft/place.

In Holland rooms of capacity greater than 50 can be termed lecture halls and Ministry of Education standards are:

50 places at 1·3 sq.m/place (14·0 sq.ft)
to   200 places at 0·8 sq.m/place (8·6 sq.ft)
400 places at 1·0 sq.m/place (10·8 sq.ft) to allow for extra gangways

These represent the official maximum levels recognised by various grant-giving organisations as a means of controlling schemes submitted to them. They must also necessarily be arbitrary levels which will encompass a suitable variety of different lecture hall types.

A sample of lecture rooms for science and technology as built at the universities of Birmingham, Cambridge, Hull, Leicester and Manchester showed that the area per place followed a fairly well-defined curve (Fig. 26*a*). Over a capacity of 120 the area of rooms was well within the limits of U.G.C. allowance and was often achieved at an apparent reduction of one to two square feet per place.

The net floor spaces as built were:

80 places at 11·0 to 13·0 sq.ft/place
160 places at 9·0 to 10·5 sq.ft/place
240 places at 8·5 to 10·0 sq.ft/place
320 places at 8·0 to 9·5 sq.ft/place

1. It is common practice to refer to lecture spaces under 100, or flat floored, as 'rooms' and to those over 100 with stepped floors as 'theatres'.   2. Bibl. 63, p. 12.   3. Bibl. 64, p. 13.

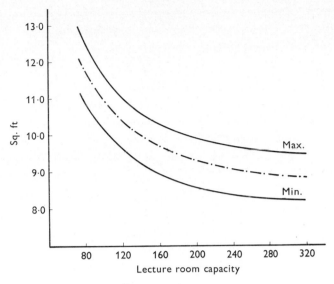

Fig. 26(*a*). Space per place as built in existing U.K. science lecture theatres. Graph showing bandwidth of observed values and average line. Information from Messrs Monk and Dunstone, Quantity Surveyors.

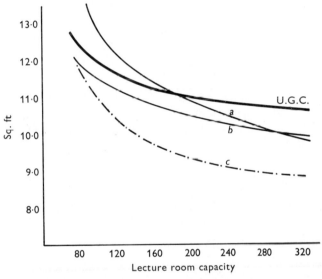

Fig. 26(*b*). Existing space per place in U.K. *c*, compared with recommendations of N.V. Bureau vor Bouwprogrammas *a*, Institut fur Schulbau Aachen *b*, and U.G.C. allocation levels.

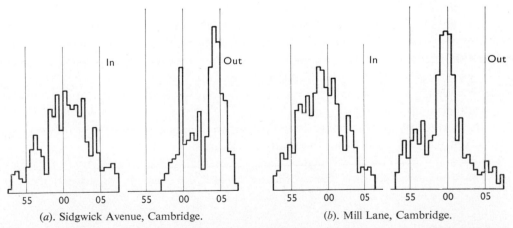

(*a*). Sidgwick Avenue, Cambridge.   (*b*). Mill Lane, Cambridge.

Fig. 27. The pattern of student movement in and out of lecture blocks during the ten minute changeover period between lectures. From information compiled by Messrs Flint and Neill, Consulting Engineers.

In Germany a range of Natural Science lecture rooms from twelve universities showed that, for capacities from 150 to 450, floor areas varied from 11 to 7 sq.ft per place and approximated to the same line of curve as above.[1]

A recently published book on laboratory planning included a limited section on lecture rooms and theatres—seen as an area of departmental space—and suggested that for theatres from 30 to 300 the areas per place should vary from 10 to 17 sq.ft/person and that for large theatres a reasonable minimum is approximately 8 sq.ft/person.[2] But what are the standards that these and other existing figures are based on, what can the lecture theatre provide for a 'reasonable' minimum, and what is the effect of applying different criteria?

Questions such as these prompted the planning consultants to T.H. Delft to evaluate standards for space allocation based on different row spacings and widths of seat. And at Bochum University where a theoretical range of room sizes was prepared on the basis of use (see Chapter 4, Section *b*) an analysis of space required for these was made[3] and the room criteria carefully defined to a standard specification, e.g.

> Projection of triple comparison images
> Image edge angles 40° minimum
> Seating from 1·4W to 6W
> Projection area in centre of hall

The resultant curve of space (Fig. 26*b*) required per place for the range (minimum) showed an interesting divergence from German grant allocation levels. In particular if these requirements for visual presentation were applied not just to science lecture theatres but to the humanities as well then, for the latter, grant levels were shown to be insufficient. This was particularly important for Bochum where the principle proposed of standard 'withdrawable' lecture theatres used to their maximum efficiency calls for such theatres to be equipped to meet a wide range of requirements and to be of uniform specification.

The survey of English science lecture rooms (see Chapter 6, Section *b*) has already shown that a large number of these rooms might need extra space at the front if, for instance, overhead writing projectors were to be built into the demonstration bench as suggested by the report on Audio Visual Aids in Higher Education.[4] Other examples of criteria which will have an effect on lecture room area are:

1 Room proportion, i.e. for rectangular planform length:breadth. (Suggestions published for relationships of between 1:1·3 and 1:1·7 indicate areas fairly square in forms.[5])

2 The standards of seating. This can either be bench, individual tip-up seats, or swivel chairs behind desk tops; all these may require different amounts of space per place. The spacing of rows can either be wide to continental standards for unlimited row length or kept to a minimum with the use of tip-up writing surfaces.

3 The standards of gangway and circulation space. Necessary widths to meet by-law requirements together with provision for back access for latecomers to a lecture. Whether it is desirable to have a gangway across the room either at the back or half-way up for larger theatres.

4 The needs of film and slide projection. Either to have a separate projection booth or to provide an area within the lecture room itself.

5 Particular requirements for demonstration space and surrounding area. This may have special relevance in new theatres where a system of movable trolleys is required in relation to a fixed services console (Figs. 28*a*, *b*).

1. Bibl. 76, Appendix.   2. Bibl. 82, p. 80.   3. Bibl. 78, Tables 6 and 7.
4. Bibl. 10, p. 53.   5. Bibl. 83, p. 278.

The study of criteria such as these suggests that it should be possible to establish conditions for lecture-room space requirements in more general terms which could then be varied to test out a given situation. A proposed methodology for this is given in Chapter 8 together with different sets of criteria applied as the basis for comparison studies.

Related areas

Allied to any lecture theatre there are likely to be one or a series of dependent or related areas. At its simplest the lecture room embedded in a Science departmental building may have a single adjacent room for the preparation of experiments. At its most complex the lecture room may be one of a group of similar rooms forming a compact teaching building and ancillary spaces may include:

   (i) Preparation room (Figs. 29*c, d*), projection and translation rooms
  (ii) Lobbies, foyers (Fig. 29*a*), waiting areas, cloakrooms, W.C.s
 (iii) Staff, cleaners' and janitors' rooms
 (iv) Plantroom (Fig. 29*b*), duct areas, fume cupboards

In addition the lecture rooms may be one of a group of teaching spaces which can include private study areas, seminar rooms and departmental museum or display areas. For the sciences, lecture rooms will also have to be related to the teaching and research laboratories where staff and students will spend the greater part of their working time and research and teaching experiments are in progress.

For the traditional situation of one or a small number of lecture rooms in a departmental building, fully controlled by that department, some or most of these ancillary spaces will form part of the building programme and some, such as the plant and circulation areas, will be shared with the general needs of all the building users. In this way the requirements of ancillary spaces for lecture rooms have been able to be absorbed within the general grant allocation levels allowed by the U.G.C. for Science building of net space + 60% (of the net) = allowable gross area.[1]

This has meant that the architect and client have been required to 'lose' any special requirements stemming from the lecture room(s) in the general bulk of individual departmental buildings. (With the exception of preparation, projection and translation space which is recognised as net or usable area.)

No particular standards of space for these ancillary areas have ever been suggested for grant allocation in Great Britain and every particular building has had to be justified individually on its merits. As a result the fluctuation of ancillary areas from department to department is considerable. Sample surveys[2] suggest that for lecture theatres built within existing science buildings, i.e. 'embedded':

1. Preparation areas approximate to 1 to 2 sq.ft/lecture place. Comparable figures for preparation room areas in other countries show:

Physics departments in U.S.A. (from 16 universities)[3]   3·1 sq.ft/lecture place
Natural Science lecture rooms in Germany since 1953   2·3 sq.ft/lecture place
   (from 14 universities)[4]

In Germany recognised grant allocation levels allow as much as 0·3 sq.m (3·23 sq.ft) per place and model recommendations[5] suggest as preparation space for science lecture theatres: Physics, Geology, Mineralogy   approx. 2·2 sq.ft/place
                Chemistry, Biology   approx. 3·2 sq.ft/place

1. Bibl. 63, p. 15.
2. From information analysed by Messrs Monk and Dunstone, Quantity Surveyors.
3. Bibl. 84, Chapter 4.   4. Bibl. 76, Appendix; 77, Appendix.   5. Bibl. 64.

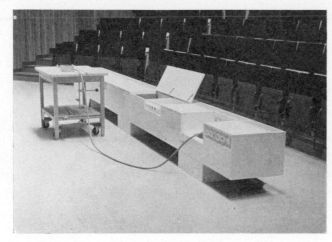

(*a*). Delft, Physics (350).

(*b*). Bristol, Physics (250).

Fig. 28. Provision of extra lecture-room space for special demonstration area requirements.

Fig. 29(*a*). Bristol. Foyer space for group of lecture theatres in new Chemistry department, 800 places.

Fig. 29(*b*). Manchester. Mechanical ventilation plant in area beneath rake of lecture theatre. Although an economical use of volume there are considerable problems of sound transfer.

Fig. 29(*c*). Durham. Typical preparation space close to Chemistry lecture theatre. Also having to serve as storage for visual aids.

Fig. 29(*d*). Delft. Preparation area common to four Physics lecture rooms with total of 1,200 places.

2. Circulation space directly attributable to individual lecture theatres is for Great Britain in the range:

> At capacities   80 to 100   4 to 6 sq.ft/lecture place
> At capacities   Over 200   3 to 4 sq.ft/lecture place

(includes foyer, lobbies, cloakrooms but excluding W.C.s, storerooms).

If, however, lecture rooms are built in separate groups or lecture blocks having their own ancillary and service spaces then the implication of a lack of recognised standards becomes clear. Given a group of lecture rooms where the net space might average 12 sq.ft per place to include preparation then, if the space standards for science buildings (gross = 160% net) currently used in Great Britain were applied, approximately 7·2 sq.ft per place would remain as basis for all ancillary space including interior walls, ducts, etc. Would such a level be sufficient for a building now acting as a concentration for student movement and activity?

Figures from other countries suggest that they would not. In Germany a figure of 240% of the net is accepted for gross floor area for 'multi-storey lecture blocks' and represents the highest allocation of ancillary space (140% of net) to any building type. For the university of Bochum the foyer to the central science lecture block (i.e. the withdrawn theatres) is being designed to a minimum of 1:1 with the (net) space within the lecture rooms. For the related groups of Natural Sciences theatres the foyers, W.C.s and cloakrooms are being designed to 11·8 sq.ft per lecture place and waiting areas at 2 sq.ft/lecture place. In Holland it is accepted practice to work to 10·8 sq.ft/lecture place for allowance of stairs, foyers and corridors.

Where designs have been prepared in the U.K. for multi-storey science lecture blocks an analysis showed that the amount of space (average) for foyers, stairs and circulation was 6·2 sq.ft/place.

> From   University of Manchester (Roscoe Bldg.)   2,300 places (built)[1]
> Brunel University (Phase 1)   2,110 places (project)
> University of Leeds   2,650 places (project)

In each case further space was needed for cloakrooms, W.C.s, storage, ducts, plant-rooms, interval walls, etc. which would suggest that a figure of over 10 sq.ft per place would be needed for all circulation and ancillary accommodation. This would require that the gross area for lecture blocks needs to be over 200% net.

Essentially the grouping together of lecture rooms into a complete building unit represents a distinct and comparatively new building type. This means a new pattern of use and a very high concentration of student movement. It is suggested that the foyers of a lecture block represent a function of use of the building which requires an adequate and recognised allocation of space. The two strongest arguments for this are:

1   At interchange times, if a group of lecture rooms is used efficiently at 60% occupancy of rooms, there may easily occur a situation where students representing 50% of the nominal places in the building are leaving and a further 50% are arriving for the next lecture. A survey of existing lecture blocks revealed the considerable overlap during a 10 min interchange between those arriving for lectures before others had left (this was in part due to lectures ending at varying times and the arrival peak being spread over 5 to 6 min). As a result the circulation may well have to cope with the nominal capacity of the building as a throughput in a very limited time (Fig. 27).

1. Bibl. 34, p. 201.

2   As well as merely going to and from lectures the very act of grouping a number of teaching areas together suggests the possibility of discussion and student contact between and after those lectures. There are strong arguments for optimising such contact (see Chapter 2, Section *b*) and perhaps to encourage it further with the use of adequate waiting areas and a series of identifiable spaces through which student movement is channelled.[1]

So far the planning requirements for related or ancillary spaces have been discussed with reference to the single lecture room or to a group of lecture rooms. It is, however, essential to distinguish also between possible types of teaching room groupings and their related needs:

1   The monolithic lecture block for 2,000 to 3,000 places having several large lecture rooms and a variety of smaller sizes down to the classroom. A type already built in the U.K., e.g. at Manchester and with several similar buildings now in the design stage, possessing preparation rooms, workshop space, projection rooms, staff and janitor's rooms, foyers and coffee bar.[2]

2   A smaller lecture grouping of say 800 to 1,000 places but remaining an individual building block. Proposed as a series of standardised 'nodal' points in relation to science buildings with potential for alteration/addition. Less emphasis on preparation space and possibly with only small or intermediate size theatres all on one floor level allowing circulation pattern to be simple. Basic ancillary accommodation which could also include seminar rooms or study carrells allied to the structure above or below main level.

3   The 'communications' centre, for which several schemes are now in the design stage in the U.S.A., where the emphasis is on a large and complex grouping of teaching and originating spaces with colloquium rooms and self study facilities. Requiring large preparation and storage areas in connection with televised presentation together with possible turntable stages and back projection areas.[3]

This third category, which has originated in America under the stimulus of television and the use of mechanical aids to teaching, has already reached the stage of evolution into a new building type. (See Chapter 2, Section *b*.) This type has as its primary design criteria the exposition of carefully prepared and pre-rehearsed televisual items; for this a whole range of originating and ancillary spaces, e.g. studios, sets, rehearsal rooms, etc. are required to support the process. As a result a building programme with new sets of standards emerged which it would be a mistake to try and see just as a further development of existing lecture facilities and the likely pattern for future lecture rooms and groupings. On the contrary if the relevance of the lecture is accepted, and in particular for the sciences (this is discussed in Chapter 1, Section *a*), then the two categories of teaching building will need to exist in parallel each satisfying a different set of planning, and therefore space use, requirements.

1. Bibl. 4, p. 353.　　2. Bibl. 52, p. 206; 31, p. 281.　　3. See Bibl. 10, p. 14; 75, pt. III; 13, p. 178.

8. A METHOD OF MATHEMATICAL ANALYSIS PROPOSED

The lecture theatre, in common with other types of auditoria, represents an architectural volume that can be subject to mathematical definition. Once the levels or standards of room planning criteria are agreed upon it is possible to delineate the plan and section of the lecture room in regard to 'presentation' and 'support' requirements (see Chapter 6, Section *a*). Exact values can, for instance, be placed on:

Viewing angles to screen images
Distance to nearest eye (limits)
Distance to furthest eye
Seat dimensions
Row spacings
Demonstrations area dimensions
Gangway and exit widths
Screen size in relation to image size
Height of screen above floor level
Required volume of room per place (maximum and minimum)

As a result, given any one general requirement for a lecture room, e.g.

Capacity   Room area   Dimensions

it is possible to derive the others to satisfy the planning criteria.

Example. A lecture room is required of rectangular planform of capacity 160. Distance to nearest eye to be 2W and farthest 6W and image on front wall to subtend maximum angle to normal of 45° in plan

If nearest eye is 2W away and centre image angle 45°
then for a straight front row length approximately $= 4W$

therefore at 2 ft seat widths places per row $= \dfrac{4W}{2}$ (S)

Number of rows at $2\frac{3}{4}$ ft spacing to farthest row $= \dfrac{6W - 2W}{2\frac{3}{4}}$ (N)

but N × S = Capacity in places, therefore Capacity $= \dfrac{4W}{2} \times \dfrac{6W - 2W}{2\frac{3}{4}}$ (K)

$$= \frac{32}{11} W^2.$$

Therefore for given capacity the required screen image size is

$$\sqrt{\left(\frac{11}{32} K\right)} \quad \text{for } 2W/6W \text{ at } 45° \text{ limits.}$$

Therefore for K = 160:   W $\simeq$ 7·4 ft,
N $\simeq$ 10·8 rows,
S $\simeq$ 14·8 places.

Obviously these figures must be translated as whole numbers and will approximate, therefore, to the required capacity. For instance, this example can be answered by a block of seats 15 by 11 rows. Also

Depth of room $= 2\frac{3}{4}N + (2W - 2)$ if eye is 2 ft behind front of row   (L)
Breadth of room $= 2S + 8$ if two 4 ft aisles assumed   (B)

For the above example very simple criteria have been taken but it can be understood that there are a wide variety of alternative solutions if,

Centre image angles varied, e.g. 35° or 55°
Distance to nearest eye varied, e.g. 1·75W or 2·25W
Row spacing 3 ft or any other dimension
Seat spacings 1 ft 9 in. or any other dimension

In each case one or a combination of alternatives is possible. By varying one particular value through a complete range the effect on the room form can be studied. If for the example of a room of 160 given above the width of the front row were acceptable at lengths 5W or 6W (representing wider limits for the centre image angle to the screen) then the range of alternatives could be printed:

K	Row width		Image W ft		Rows N		Places S	
160	4W		7·4		11		15	
	5W			6·7		9		17
		6W		6·2		9		18

and for a different capacity:

200	4W		8·3		12		16	
	5W			7·5		11		19
		6W		6·8		10		20

This manual programme shows, in outline, how a series of tables could be built up for different room capacities for different viewing conditions. Further values could be added for room area, distance screen to front row, etc. In fact the form of this illustration only gives an approximate value for the critical side angle positions and takes no account of difference in dimension between the actual positioning of rows to correspond with a distance to the nearest eye and the theoretical maximum dimension to the back wall. Nor are there any means of extracting values which might be beyond the acceptable limits without a careful investigation of each item of the table.

In order to cover these and other requirements, and to provide for a more flexible method of obtaining ranges of information, a mathematical programme (code named 'Seatpoint') was set up so that tables could be printed out with the use of a computer. This allowed the information to be obtained selectively and for exclusion, or 'weeding', factors to be applied so that unacceptable (i.e. beyond the working limits) material would not be printed.

The basic *assumptions* for this initial 'Seatpoint' programme were:

Rectangular planform of room
Seating in a rectangular block to back wall
Two aisles provided for at width 4 ft; no dais at front
Width of seating dictated by maximum angle to screen normal

The *variables* to be (Fig. 30):

Horizontal centre image angle (degrees)	(C)
Seat width (ft)	(P)
Row spacing (ft)	(Q)
Vertical angle from nearest eye to top of screen W + 7[1] (degrees)	(V)
Seats per row	(S)
Number of rows	(N)

1. A standard assumption has been made for these calculations that lower edge of projected image should be at + 7 ft 0 in

Capacity in places   (K)
Space front wall to front row (ft)   (T)[1]
Room width (ft)   (B)
Room length (ft)   (L)
Area (L × B) (sq.ft)   (A)

In printing out the tables values were also added for the difference D between the area of the room and that allowed for the capacity by the U.G.C. grant allocation level; this was shown as a percentage ratio D/A.

The *factors* which were taken to give a particular table were:

Image size   (W)
Room length   (in terms of W)
Distance image to nearest eye (in terms of W)

In this way the maximum flexibility and range of tables was achieved with capacity fluctuating for the various conditions. By allocating values to a range of the variables it was then possible to print out a complete series of tables and read off the other variables:

Example

For image size   4·50 ft
Room length   6·00W
Distance image to nearest eye   2·00W

Given (P) Seat width   = 2·00 ft
      (Q) Row space   = 2·75 ft

then for a range of centre image angles 40°, 45°, 50°, 55°, the following conditions are obtained:

C	P	Q	V	S	N	K	T + G	B	L	A
40	2·00	2·75	37	6	7	42	7·75	20·00 × 27·00		540
45	2·00	2·75	37	7	7	49	7·75	22·00 × 27·00		594
50	2·00	2·75	37	9	7	63	7·75	26·00 × 27·00		702
55	2·00	2·75	37	11	7	77	7·75	30·00 × 27·00		810

This table must, however, be qualified to give only information that is relevant or useful. For example:

1   If the maximum limit for the vertical angle to top of screen (V) is to be 35° none of the above planforms are satisfactory.
2   If no lecture room is required with a nominal capacity of less than 70 then only one example (at 55°) is relevant.
3   If a demonstration bench of 2 ft 6 in. with 4 ft clear space to visual aids wall and 2 ft 6 in. passing space in front is required (total 9 ft) then no value for this (T + G) is satisfactory.

The Seatpoint programme was, therefore, written so that limits could be placed on any variables and that if a particular reading went over those limits that particular line in the table would not be printed. In this way a print-out can be made extremely selective and the full benefit derived from the computer.

1. Also in order to allow for the initial premise that the room should have a maximum length as a factor of W (e.g. 6W stemming from a maximum image size subtended at the eye) and that the resultant difference between this and the assumed distance to the nearest eye was not an exact row spacing, the tolerance (i.e. gap between back row and back wall <Q) was given a value G. After fixing the row width and number of rows the block of seating is then assumed to be moved back by this amount, therefore space at front = T + G and actual distance to nearest eye = T + G + Q where for this exercise eye position taken as coincident with back of row.

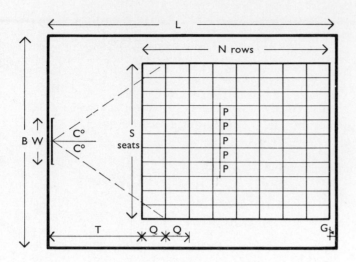

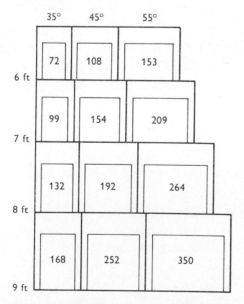

Fig. 30. The variables used in the Seatpoint computer program.

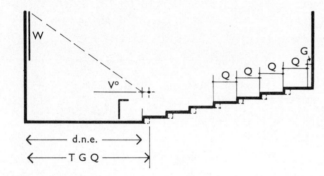

Fig. 31 (*a*). Changes in planform of the lecture room with increasing sizes of projected image. For 10° increments of centre image viewing angle.

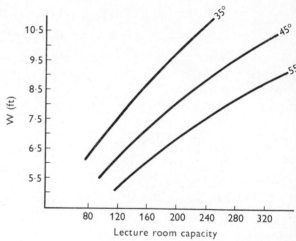

Fig. 31 (*b*). Image size to room capacity for varying viewing angle criteria.

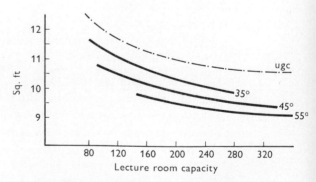

Fig. 31 (*c*). Net space per place for varying viewing angle criteria.

Figures from Seatpoint 3A print-out. Room length 6·00W d.n.e 2W.

Example

A room capacity is required of approximately 160 and between limits of 150 to 170.

Image size to be 7·00 ft.

Room length 6·00W maximum.

Provision in demonstration area for overhead projector at 1·25W from screen with a 2 ft 6 in. gangway in front.

These conditions were tested at:

> Distance to nearest eye = 1·75W, 2·00W, 2·25W.
> Centre image angles 35° to 60° at 2·5° increments.

The resultant print-out tables showed that from a possible range of 33 conditions examined there were three solutions satisfactory:

C	P	Q	V	S	N	K	T + G	B	L	A
45·0	2·00	2·75	35	14	11	154	11·75	36·00 × 42·00	1,512
47·5	2·00	2·75	35	15	11	165	11·75	38·00 × 42·00	1,596
47·5	2·00	2·75	31	17	10	170	14·50	42·00 × 42·00	1,764

Further examples of selected print-outs could be:

> Particular room size with values for B or L
> Rooms satisfying particular area A or range of areas

and this list can be extended for any condition set on one of the variables. For example, with differing values for seating dimensions P, Q:

> Image size 9·50 ft   (Factors)
> Room length 6·00W   (Factors)
> Distance image to nearest eye 1·75W   (Factors)
> Centre image angles 45°, 50°, 55°, 60° (Variables)
> Seat width 1·75 ft, 2·00 ft   (Variables)
> Row depth 2·75 ft, 3·00 ft   (Variables)
> $9·00 \text{ ft} \leqslant T + G$ (Selection)
> $0° \leqslant V \leqslant 35°$ (Selection)
> $80 \leqslant K \leqslant 320$ (Selection)

C	P	Q	V	S	N	K	T + G	B	L	A
45	1·75	2·75	35	19	15	285	15·75	41·25 × 57·00	2,351
45	1·75	3·00	35	19	14	266	15·00	41·25 × 57·00	2,351
45	2·00	2·75	35	16	15	240	15·75	40·00 × 57·00	2,280
45	2·00	3·00	35	16	14	224	15·00	40·00 × 57·00	2,280
50	1·75	3·00	35	22	14	308	15·00	46·50 × 57·00	2,651
50	2·00	2·75	35	19	15	285	15·75	46·00 × 57·00	2,622
50	2·00	3·00	35	19	14	266	15·00	46·00 × 57·00	2,622

In order to obtain a basis for comparison techniques for costing and space analysis, and to provide a pattern for the behaviour of smaller rectangular lecture planforms (capacities 80 to 320) when various criteria are altered (e.g. Fig. 31 *a*), a print-out 3A was made of the Seatpoint programme for:

> Image size 5·00 ft to 10·00 ft by 0·50 increments
> Room length 6·00W
> Distance image to nearest eye 1·75W, 2·00W, 2·25W

Centre image angles 35° to 60° by 5° increments
Seat width 2·00 ft
Row depth 2·75 ft
80 ≤ K ≤ 320
1·25W + 2·50 ft ≤ T + G space for overhead projector
9·00 ft ≤ T + G space for demonstration bench

[The full print-out for these limits is given at Appendix 1.]

Applications using Seatpoint 3A print-out

1. Given a minimum requirement for space to front row 9 ft and standards for placing of overhead projector, an inspection of the print-out showed that, for smaller image sizes, effective distance (minimum) to nearest eye was over 2W. As the image size increases and capacities go up so it is possible to obtain satisfactory solutions where this value decreases to 1·75W and below.

2. By taking a value for centre image angle (C) and following it through the range the requirement of area in terms of space per place can be plotted: if this is taken for the minimum acceptable value for d.n.e. at each size of image a graph is formed of the minimum space requirements to satisfy the presentation criteria. For example, for centre image angle of 45°:

W	K	A	d.n.e. (min.)	Space/place
5·5	96	1,056	2·25W	11·0
6·5	130	1,326	2·00W	10·2
7·5	156	1,530	1·75W	9·8
8·5	221	2,142	2·00W	9·7*
9·5	240	2,280	1·75W	9·5

* No value for 1·75W.

These figures, or a comparable set for any other criteria, can then be plotted in comparison with known levels such as the U.G.C. grant allocation figures (Fig. 32*a*).

3. If a series of comparative curves are plotted for:

area of room (net)   space per place (net)

at different values of the viewing angles a picture can be built up of the relative efficiency in use of space and this compared to existing standards. The narrower the subtended angle to the screen, e.g. 35°, the longer and narrower the room form and the better are the viewing characteristics; the space per place, however, is greater than by using a wider room with more marginal viewing characteristics, e.g. 55° (Fig. 31*c*).

4. For a given image size there are a range of possible capacities, e.g. for W = 7 ft and d.n.e. = 2·00W:

C	K	C	K
35	99	50	176
40	121	55	209
45	154	60	264

By plotting the value of capacity for a particular viewing angle it is possible to read off the potential lecture-room capacity for a given image size/viewing angle combination (Fig. 31*b*). So for a theatre of 240 the image sizes required would be approximately:

W =   7·5   ft at 55° viewing to centreline
W =   9   ft at 45° viewing to centreline
W = 10·75 ft at 35° viewing to centreline

and the minimum required front wall heights would alter correspondingly.

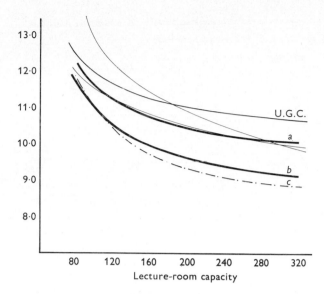

Fig. 32(*a*). Minimum acceptable values for space per place (sq. ft) in lecture room for conditions of Seatpoint program. *b*, At 2·75 ft row spacing; *a*, at 3·00 ft. Existing level in U.K. shown at *c*, and also levels as given in Fig. 26(*b*).

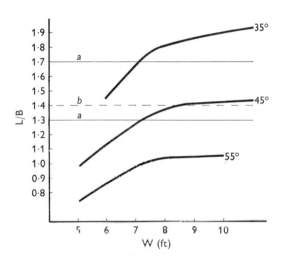

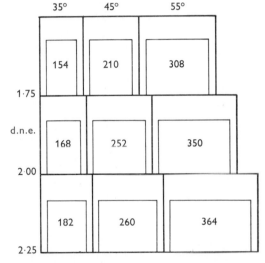

Fig. 32(*b*). Room proportion length:breadth as a function of viewing angle and image size. Limits for proportion suggested by: *b*, Munce; and *a*, Lewis.

Fig. 32(*c*). The changes in planform of the lecture room with increasing values for distance to nearest cyc. For 10° increments of centre image viewing angle at W = 9·00 ft.

Figures from Seatpoint 3A print-out.

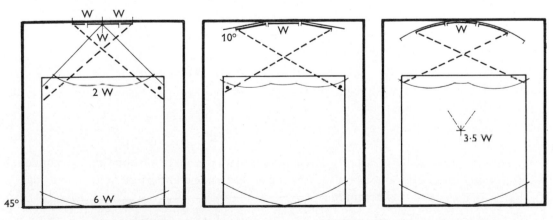

Fig. 33. Contrasted presentation of comparison images for 40° edge angle viewing. Room form as for viewing of single image W at 45°. Left: basic flat wall with two images. Centre: triple images, outer screens angled by 10°. [See *New Spaces for Learning*.] Right: triple images on 3·5W radial screen. [See Recommendations of Institut fur Schulbau, Aachen.]

5. The proportion of planform B × L varies for the requirements of viewing angle, image size and related room length (Fig. 32*c*). For instance with

$$W = 8 \text{ ft, d.n.e.} = 2.00W, \text{ and RL} = 6.00W$$

	C	B	L
	35	30·00 × 48·00	
	45	40·00 × 48·00	
	55	52·00 × 48·00	

These factors for B and L can be plotted to give a curve at any viewing angle. They can also be compared with previous empirical statements on reasonable room proportion (see Chapter 7). If this is done the suggested values of 1·3 to 1·7 are seen to include part of the curve for 35° and part for 45° thus indicating that a centre image angle of approximately 40° had been considered optimum (Fig. 32*b*).

This particular Seatpoint print-out 3A did not provide for variations of values for seat spacings but an earlier print-out had shown the different picture of area requirements if a row spacing of 3 ft instead of 2·75 ft was used. The flexibility of the programme would allow any value to be inserted and it would, for instance, be a simple matter to evaluate the possibilities of using 'continental' row spacing (18 in. clear between fixed seating) and, by an adjustment to the programme, to compare the effect of this with the need for extra gangways for traditional spacings.

Another point where this particular first programme might be required to yield further information is on the space needs if a gangway was to be placed behind the rear row of seats either for access to a projection area or to aid circulation. In this case it would be possible for the item only to be added in over a certain size/capacity.

The Seatpoint conditions also include the angle subtended to the centreline of a screen image (C) as a basic factor. While this provides a useful series of readings there may well be in the future a need for double or triple comparison images (Fig. 33) and the implications of this for the design of the screen wall have already been mentioned (see Chapter 6, Section *a*). If the critical viewing condition for comparative images is taken as a 40° angle to the farthest edge of the image, then for two images size W projected on to a flat front wall about the centreline a graphical examination based on the Seatpoint programme showed the following loss of seats due to too great an angle of vision:[1]

	Planform as for centre image angle			
W	35°	45°	55°	d.n.e.
5·5	0/72	2/96	10/136	2·25
6·5	0/90	2/130	12/180	2·00
7·5	0/110	2/165	14/231	2·00
8·5	0/143	4/221	24/312	2·00*
9·5	0/182	4/240	22/345	1·75

* No figure for 1·75W in tables.

For these conditions of projecting two comparison images on to a front wall, the number of unusable seats above need not be any higher for triple comparison images if an edge angle situation of 30° is acceptable.

1. Certain seats at the back of the room may fall within the angle of vision but beyond the room length of 6W. This situation exists throughout the programme where 6W is taken on the centreline section and not as a radial arc; if it was required that the back outside seats should be in the area 5W to 6W rather than 6W to 7W the room length value could be suitably altered.

The information for comparison testing such as this and more intricate design and presentation criteria can be written into the programme. Further sophistications in programming could, for example, amend the Seatpoint tabulation to give readings for trapezoidal planform (given the generating conditions) and relate plan, section and volume in general mathematical terms.

At this stage though the first Seatpoint tables form a sufficiently direct and practical means of reference to be considered as a general architectural planning and design tool. Values for lecture-room dimensions and criteria can be read off and quick comparisons made in an analogous way to the use of tables for calculating thermal or structural loads.

9. STUDIES FOR FLEXIBILITY OF LECTURE GROUPINGS

The concept of groups of science lecture rooms seen as nodal points in relation to a science teaching hinterland has been proposed. The studies for these groupings suggested that they might be medium size, possibly single level organisations connected to the main student and staff circulation ways and thought of in terms of common user space. At the same time no particular capacities for the rooms within these groups have been fixed and, on the contrary, the need for flexibility, potential for alteration and adaptation of lecture-room forms has been stressed (see Chapter 5).

In the previous chapter the creation of a mathematical programme for analysing rectangular lecture rooms in the range of 80 to 320 has been described. And it is from this range of room sizes that the lecture theatres comprising the Science nodes would need to be drawn.

How do the two main lines of investigation, one into the efficiency of utilisation of rooms, the other into a statement of design needs in general terms, relate to each other. And how can they most usefully be combined to form part of a set of general principles for lecture-room planning.

At the simplest level for a typical lecture room grouping,[1]

1 at 320	2 at 120
1 at 240	2 at 80
1 at 160	

a series of rooms could be selected from the Seatpoint tables (see Appendix 1) to provide a guide to the area and linear requirements. Even with a comparatively small number of choices (and the tables referred to only show 117 possible planforms) what soon becomes the major difficulty is fitting these selected theoretical diagrams together into a co-ordinated architectural design and integrating them with the systems of structure, services and movement.

If, however, the room sizes/diagrams themselves bore some mathematical relationship to each other, or fell into a series of ranges or categories, a logic of assembling the various groupings might emerge.

The key to one such system of logic is easily seen from a print-out of the computer tables where for Image size $= 7$ ft; d.n.e. $= 1.75W$:

C	N	K	B	L
35	11	88	24.00×42.00	
40	11	110	28.00×42.00	
45	11	132	32.00×42.00	
50	11	154	36.00×42.00	
55	11	187	42.00×42.00	

This indicates that, for a given room length (derived from 6W maximum) and standard room cross-section, the effect of varying the viewing angles is to give a range of room

---

1. This represents the requirement of grouped rooms for the 'average' existing U.K. science area at 20 h per week utilisation as described in Chapter 4, Section c.

capacities from 88 to 187 (Fig. 34a) and the possibility of combining rooms on this range together. So a plan area of 60·00 ft × 42·00 ft could be filled by:

$$24·00 × 42·00 (K = 88) + 36·00 × 42·00 (K = 154)$$

or

$$28·00 × 42·00 (K = 110) + 32·00 × 42·00 (K = 132)$$

The way in which a series of number combinations can be built up from a table of this sort is demonstrated with:

Image size 6·00 ft
d.n.e = 2·00W
Room length = 36·00 ft

C (°)	K	B (ft)	Combination of room widths possible (pairs)					
35	72	24	24+24	—	—	—	—	—
40	90	28	24+28	28+28	—	—	—	—
45	108	32	24+32	28+32	*32+32*	—	—	—
50	126	36	*24+36*	*28+36*	*32+36*	*36+36*	—	—
55	153	42	24+42	28+42	32+42	36+42	*42+42*	—
60	180	48	*24+48*	28+48	32+48	*36+48*	42+48	48+48

(The figures in italic show where pairs of values are interchangeable with another of the same value.)

A series of number combinations such as these can be formed for any particular table of image size, room length and distance to the nearest eye. Their value lies in the flexibility to form different groups of room sizes in any one set; as a result a strip of lecture rooms of a given length could be divided in a variety of different ways, i.e. from the above table:

capacities	72	72	72	72	–	96 ft
		108	108	108	=	96 ft
		90		108	126	= 96 ft
		72		90	153	= 96 ft (see Fig. 34b)

No one table from 35° to 55° (a reasonable maximum viewing angle) gives a complete range of room capacities from 80 to 320:

W = 6·00 at 2·00W d.n.e.   72 to 153
W = 8·00 at 2·00W d.n.e.   132 to 264
W = 9·00 at 2·00W d.n.e.   168 to 350

As a result if viewing angles up to 55° were acceptable and a range of rooms required including those for 80 and 320 two or possibly three standard cross-sections would be required. Within the limits of any of these sections chosen there would be a wide variety of choices for room capacity, or combination of capacity, as indicated above.

The application to design of these number patterns can be seen by reference back to the typical groupings of rooms suggested for selection from the Seatpoint tables:

1 at 320   2 at 120
1 at 240   2 at 80
1 at 160

If these are now chosen from only two sectional ranges the design and structuring systems are given a basic order. There is, however, no particular set of solutions that result from this and outside considerations such as existing grid layouts, size of groupings likely, relation to hinterland buildings, number of storeys, can be used for selection.

A typical answer might be:

	K	B × L
W = 9 ft 0 in. d.n.e. 2·25W	260	48·00 × 54·00 (45°)
	312	56·00 × 54·00 (50°)
W = 7 ft 0 in. d.n.e. 1·75W	88	24·00 × 42·00 (35°)
	110	28·00 × 42·00 (40°)
	154	36·00 × 42·00 (50°)

(these are taken from tables produced for W by increments of 1 ft. A closer fit to the capacities can be obtained from a wider choice of tables).

In practice it will be likely that the ranges of rooms chosen will have to be formed into a compact building block. The most direct solution could be to have the two sectional types (in the above example) as two parts of the building with common space, e.g. foyers or preparation areas between them (Fig. 34*c*). Similar section rooms (and therefore of similar structural systems) could also be placed one above another if a multi-storey block was required.

To achieve this compactness the total length of run of any section, i.e. range, will be of interest for comparison with the length of another section opposing it or being placed above it. A great variety of size and dimension combinations has already been shown to be possible and a further adjustment to any particular range of room capacity lies in the choice of the sectional form relating breadth to length, e.g. lecture rooms of approximately 80, 120, 160, could, for the above example, equally well have been chosen as:

W = 6 ft 0 in. d.n.e. 2·00W	K (nom)	B × L
	90 (80)	28·00 × 36·00 (40°)
	126 (120)	36·00 × 36·00 (50°)
	150 (160)	42·00 × 36·00 (55°)

to yield a set of dimensions of greater width.

So far the selection of lecture-room dimensions has been considered in terms of single room units, each a finite volume, although having a common length and section with other rooms in a range. In doing this a method of rationalisation for a wide variety of possible planforms and volumes has been aimed at. However, the strongest case for considering lecture rooms for grouping in a series of ranges is the inherent flexibility for change and addition which such an approach would allow, and which has already been proposed as a basic principle for medium science lecture groupings.

The main object of lecture-room flexibility will be to alter the size of rooms, e.g. 2 at 100 to 1 at 200. It can be:

1   Immediate (i.e. 5 to 10 min) and usually seen in the form of a folding partition or moving wall which will amalgamate two spaces into one.
2   Single period alteration (i.e. approximately 1 h) by means of more complex moving or rotating elements (Fig. 36).
3   Short-term by removal or addition of non-structural elements; probably possible during a vacation.
4   Long-term by structural rebuilding or alteration.

This concept of flexibility is closely related to the evolution and teaching pattern of the university and, as the university programme changes, so a particular block of rooms might need:

additional rooms added
room capacities altered
total size reduced

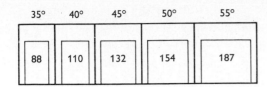

Fig. 34(a). Variation of room sizes for a range of maximum viewing angles. For $W = 7$ ft, d.n.e. $= 1 \cdot 75W$ and $R \, L = 6W$.

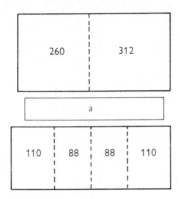

Fig. 34(c). Two ranges of rooms for $W = 9$ ft and $W = 7$ ft opposed to form a grouping with common foyer space a.

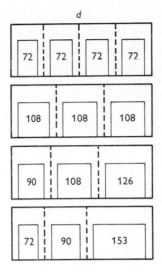

Fig. 34(b). Combinations of room size that can be formed for a given length of rooms, d, of given section. For $W = 6$ ft, d.n.e. $= 2 \cdot 00W$ and $R \, L = 6W$.

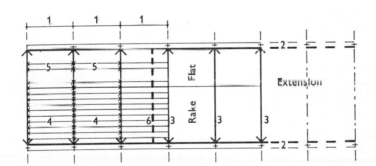

Fig. 35. The structural implications to provide flexibility for alterations to room widths in a given range such as that above d. 1, Structural grid module. 2, Zone for vertical supports and services to correspond with chosen room section of the range. 3, Primary beams lying in section between ceiling and floor. 4, Standard floor and ceiling units stepped relative to each other where necessary. 5, Special services floor duct in demonstration area. 6, Infill cross-walls able to be supported wherever required in future alterations.

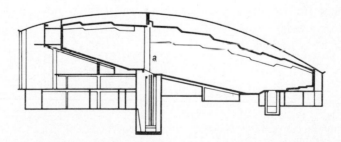

Fig. 36. An example of rapid flexibility by means of a complex vertical sliding wall at a. Main auditorium at University of Hamburg for 1,800, divisible into two spaces of 1,200 and 600.

A recent survey and statistical analysis of lecture rooms at the rapidly growing University of Hull emphasised this, for the findings proposed that a large number of smaller rooms should be built first which could later be easily converted into fewer rooms of two or three times their initial capacity.

An answer to this type of planning problem could be provided with the system of ranges of standard section lecture rooms if the walls between them were considered as impermanent non-structural items rather than as one side of a structural box. By doing this a given length of rooms could be altered to suit any combination of room capacities/dimensions that would fit it,[1] e.g. a range of rooms

$$77 \quad 77 \quad 77 \quad 77 \quad 77$$

of depth 6W for W = 5 ft 0 in. could, by altering cross-walls, become

$$91 \quad 112 \quad 112 \quad 91$$

without disturbing the remainder of the building envelope.

The most immediate implication of this would be for the design of an extendable structural system achieving back and front walls, floor and roof suitably cross-braced but with no supports within the sectional area of the room. This system would also need to allow for standard seat/audience loadings anywhere on the floor deck and for the support of non-loadbearing cross-walls at a small standard increment of spacing. Such a system could also provide for extension or reduction by structural bays and for a similar system to be placed over it on the same grid (Fig. 35). Its detailed structural dimensions could be chosen to suit any requirement of sectional form and range.[2] Once built it would act as the arbiter of future patterns of change and addition possible for that particular group of lecture rooms.

The lecture room has traditionally been seen as one of the most permanent and specially designed items of university plant, and not as a subject for industrialised building. However, the studies for the application of general principles to the planning and design of lecture groupings have shown how preferred ranges of room size can be selected to act as a basis for future flexibility. Within the system certain solutions may prove more useful than others (e.g. a progression of room sizes approximating to increments of 40) and certain building elements may have a wider range of application in different situations.

This suggests that the concept of flexibility might be extended from the planning of lecture-room groupings to the actual methods of construction by:

1   Prefabrication techniques
2   Dimensional analysis

In the example given in this section the need for future alteration/adaptation was shown to act as a major influence in writing the programme for the structural requirements. From this it is apparent that there could be a number of standard building elements based on the need for a uniform room section for any range of rooms. If, as has been suggested, a satisfactory 'basic' series of room combinations could be selected with three such ranges, for instance:

$$
\begin{aligned}
W &= 6\cdot00 & RL &= 36\cdot00 \text{ ft} \\
&= 8\cdot00 & &= 48\cdot00 \text{ ft} \\
&= 9\cdot00 & &= 54\cdot00 \text{ ft}
\end{aligned}
$$

1. For the limited number of occasions on which a university would wish to make such a rearrangement of a particular grouping the level of flexibility of Category 3 (p. 92) would be sufficient.
2. As suggested earlier there should also be the opportunity for seminar spaces or study carrells to be added at upper or lower levels.

and for all these the structural bay width was kept standard, then items such as floor steppings or secondary roof beams could also be kept standard. Other items which might then be subject to dimensional co-ordination as part of this system could be:

Increments of spacing for cross-wall positioning
Seat fixings
Front wall units   display sections
                    door units
                    service units
Rear wall units   infill sections
                    projection box units
Cross-wall panels for demonstration area
                    for stepped section
Main structural framework

The selection of dimensions for any range of elements such as this could be related to existing proposals for modular co-ordination within the building industry and the use of the 4 in. module (M). For general planning use the computer tables have shown that a wide range of choice is available for variations of room width of 2 ft 0 in. (6M). This dimension, which equalled the preferred seat spacing and would act as a location key for wall and row fixings, could be used as a multi-modular setting grid to which the various primary and secondary units could relate. It would also, in conjunction with other preferred modular dimensions, become the basis for the sizing of manufacturers fittings and equipment which at present can show wide dimensional variations.

With this stage a set of principles for the planning of science lecture-room groupings has now been covered. It has been shown how a set of lecture sizes, coming from an analysis of utilisation factors, can be selected from the computer tables to satisfy given presentation criteria. These can then be analysed as ranges of rooms for future growth and change, a structural system defined to meet their requirements and finally this system related to the needs of industrialised building. In the next section these principles are applied to the problems of comparative costing of lecture theatres.

IV
COST OF THE SCIENCE LECTURE ROOM

10. PLANNING FACTORS INFLUENCING COSTS

During the five years 1957–62 the expenditure on university building projects in the U.K. approved for non-recurrent grants by the U.G.C.[1] was £124·7 million of which

> 73 % building and fees
> 22 % furniture and equipment
> 5 % sites and properties

Of this approximately £68·5 million (55 %) was for Pure and Applied Science Buildings.

The 1965 edition of *Notes on Procedure* for obtaining Non-Recurrent Grants published by the U.G.C. showed that basic Grant allowance levels for building other than residential (e.g. Science) was calculated from a starting rate of ninety-six shillings per sq.ft of gross area.[2] For pure science buildings this gross area is arrived at as:

> usable space + 60 % usable (termed the 'balance' area)

This represents a basic cost within which the architect will be required to provide the agreed usable area complete with nominal heating and ventilation, floor finishes, lighting, plumbing, sanitary fittings, drainage, external works and such fittings as are needed for the functioning of the 'balance' areas. (All other fittings are set against a special account.)

In addition for most building types extra costs can be allowed, e.g. if specialised services, excessive floor loads, unusual spans or ceiling heights are shown to be needed. This, for instance, would be the case with Science teaching or research laboratories heavily serviced and with the need for wide structure free areas. It would also be true for science lecture rooms, which receive no specific reference elsewhere, and which would come within this category.

An annual review of prices within the building industry[3] showed that for 1965 the average rate per sq.ft for university science buildings in the U.K. was:

		Shillings per sq.ft (gross)*
Laboratories	Chemistry	185
	Engineering	155
	Physics	150

* Price exclusive of fittings.

This represented the cost of buildings in practice and the average level which would need to be met from the U.G.C. initial allowance of 96*s*. per sq.ft (gross) plus further justified extras and abnormals.

No indication is given of the relative cost attributable to the lecture room, either for

1. Bibl. 43, p. 52.
2. Bibl. 63, p. 16.
3. From *Spons Price Book* (1965–66), ed. Davis Belfield and Everest, London.

arts or science use, although in practice it is generally accepted that it is likely to be an expensive item of building by reason of:

> large floor and roof spans[1]
> stepped section—probably varying
> extra height and related structure
> acoustic form and insulation

Further costs are likely to be added in planning to achieve reasonable minimum standards of function and circulation, e.g.

> design to exploit visual aids
> no daylighting or opening windows
> back access for students
> finishes for correct acoustics
> mechanical ventilation and filtered air
> cooling if for continuous summer use
> extra servicing for demonstration use

As has been already referred to the science lecture room traditionally has been 'embedded' in departmental and laboratory buildings and the cost absorbed in the total allowed cost. This has meant that the price for standard science teaching buildings has necessarily included for the provision of these specialised volumes with their servicing and non-standard structural needs. Inevitably where a typical department may have 6,000 sq.ft net of lecture space to 85,000 sq.ft of other net space one type of accommodation may have to be subsidised at the expense of the other.

One result of this absorption of cost of the 'embedded' lecture room has been that where cost information on lecture rooms is later required it is extremely hard or even impossible to retrieve unless this was specially considered at the pricing stage. In consequence the published information available on the cost of lecture rooms is extremely slight; where it has been reported it is usually because the room has been 'extracted' architecturally from its parent building or else has been added later as a separate contract.

Examples of cost analysis for such 'extracted' individual rooms confirm that with servicing, mechanical ventilation and other special items the science lecture room will be much more expensive than the related teaching laboratories in the hierarchy of university building types.[2] What such random analyses cannot give any value to is the added effect on cost of the varied design decisions, e.g.

> 'embedded' or 'extracted' volumes
> single or grouped rooms
> large rooms or small rooms

If the lecture room becomes extracted from the departmental building to form part of a lecture block, i.e. where it is a principal element, the general interdependence for costing between lecture room and department is removed and suggests that:

1 Cost of all ancillary space related to the lecture rooms must be directly carried.
2 Higher cost of lecture rooms reflected in a higher total rate per ft super for the building.
3 Extra costs incurred through the need for a separate building envelope and identity.

1. See cost studies by R.I.C.S. 'Wilderness Group'.　　2. Bibl 27, p. 357.

This certainly seems to be established in the few details that are available for this type of building in the U.K., e.g.

> Science lecture blocks at Manchester University, Manchester College of Science and Technology and proposals for Leeds and Brunel Universities

These are all large monolithic structures with a finite architectural expression, each planned for over 2,000 students and becoming one of the largest of the specially designed buildings on the campus (as opposed to areas of standard repetitive teaching buildings).

At the same time a rational look at their programmes suggests that rooms previously scattered singly will, by virtue of amalgamation, be subject to certain overall economies through:

sharing of ancillary spaces
shared insulation (walls, floors, etc.)
grouping of services, plant rooms
centralisation of teaching aids
common structural interdependence
amalgamation of circulation patterns

These economies would, therefore, reflect the difference in cost between providing a given number of individual lecture rooms, where the cost of their construction and functioning was directly attributed to them, and the same number and size of rooms formed into one or a series of lecture blocks.

For science area development such economies, if established, could be considered as providing for:

1 Higher permissible cost standards for grouped rooms than for equivalent individual or 'embedded' rooms.
2 Extra space and finance for hinterland teaching areas where awkward shapes, volumes and foyer areas extracted. (Conversely for an overall development the savings made possible by compact planning of teaching buildings can be distributed towards the lecture groupings and to those extra requirements, e.g. foyers, circulation which are a product of their concentration.)
3 A greater number of lecture places to be built for a given sum. This must be seen in conjunction with the utilisation standards which are likely to be realisable through the centralisation and grouping of rooms (see Chapter 4, Section c).

In general terms there is also the potential for a saving of capital cost in any university development by directly attributable savings in the organisation of the buildings. If, for instance, a greater efficiency of use were able to halve the number of lecture rooms required in a traditional departmental building this might mean a saving in cost of 10% to 15% (see *Manchester School*[1] where Professor B. R. Williams makes this point for Arts, i.e. unserviced rooms).

1. Bibl. 60, p. 188.

11. STUDIES FOR A COMPARISON OF COSTS

For a study of the cost of science lecture rooms either as

> Individual rooms embedded in teaching buildings
> Groups of rooms as separate buildings

it was necessary to establish a standard basis for comparison. As this was not available either in existing data or in examples of the required building types a series of theoretical models were proposed as the only valid means of analysis.

First a range of nominal room sizes between 80 and 320 at increments of 40 (see Chapter 4, Section c) were taken as corresponding to the existing spectrum of use in the U.K. universities and also as providing suitable sizes for any future projections.

From the computer tables already established (Seatpoint print-out 3A) a reasonable approximation of room planforms on a rectangular range were chosen for room length of 6W:

K	(Nominal)	W (ft)	B × L	Area	Area/place
320	(320)	10	48 × 60	2,880	9·0
272	(280)	10	42 × 60	2,520	9·3
240	(240)	9·5	40 × 57	2,280	9·5
192	(200)	8	40 × 48	1,920	10·0
165	(160)	7·5	38 × 45	1,710	10·4
117	(120)	6	34 × 36	1,224	10·5
77	(80)	5	30 × 30	900	11·7

These were taken as having 2 ft 9 in. by 2 ft 0 in. seat spacing, artificially lit and mechanically ventilated. They represent, however, nothing more than space; to function as lecture rooms as part of a teaching building, they must be allied to certain ancillary spaces. These were compiled as follows:

Foyer	5·5 to 3·0 sq.ft/place	From analysis of existing lecture rooms—by interpolation on graph for required sizes (see Chapter 7)
Plant room		From series of models for minimum requirements prepared
Tank space		by the Quantity Surveyors and Consulting Engineers
Wall thickness		
Prep. room	1·0 sq.ft/place	From observed average levels in the U.K. (see Chapter 7). These were not included for two smallest size rooms

It was assumed that areas such as W.C.s, cloakrooms, staff, stores would already be included in the supporting teaching buildings and no extra cost was added for them. From these figures the following build-up of minimum necessary Gross internal floor areas was achieved (see Appendix 2 A):

	Minimum gross internal floor area						
Room Size	77	117	165	192	240	272	320
Total F.S.	1,805*	2,216*	2,976	3,306	3,856	4,420	5,062
F.S./place	23·4	18·9	18·0	17·2	16·1	16·2	15·8

* Prep. space not included for rooms of 80 or 120 (nominal).

With this basis of space requirements (gross) compiled for each size of lecture theatre, it was then possible to make an elemental analysis of cost (e.g. for Foundations, Frame, Services, Finishes, etc.). This was achieved by considering each lecture theatre and its ancillary space as an individual and self-sufficient building unit, preparing drawings for these and then taking off approximate quantities.

The building rates for each element were taken by the Quantity Surveyors at current market prices and these costs, as a proportion of the cost of the total building unit, provided the rate per F.S. given in detail at Appendix 2 c. This form of measurement for each increment of lecture room size gave the following overall figures:

Cost analysis: Individual lecture rooms

Room size	77	117	165	192	240	272	320
Cost: Total £	15,925	18,625	23,705	26,369	30,056	32,917	35,994
Per F.S. s.	176·45	168·09	159·31	159·58	155·85	148·95	142·21
Per place, £	206·8	159·2	143·7	137·3	125·2	121·0	112·5

As a result a useful basis is established[1] for comparing the cost of different size lecture theatres either as relative price per place or per unit of area, e.g.

$$4 \text{ at } 80 \text{ (nominal)} = 1 \cdot 8 \times \text{cost of 1 at 320}$$

Or alternatively four small rooms (80) can be seen to provide 320 places at an extra cost of approximately 84% per place compared with one equivalent room (320).

The table also provides the rates of change in cost importance of the various elements needed for building individual lecture rooms. It shows how the uneven cost differential between standard increments of room size is a reflection of variations in the elemental costs. (A typical example of this can be seen for the mechanical plant where in the room size range 170 to 190 there is a change in requirement to larger fans giving a resultant increase in the F.S. rate.) See Appendix 2 c.

The main application of this build-up of element costs is, however, to provide a basis for a comparison of costs between different sizes of lecture groupings, considered as compact building blocks, and their equivalent in lecture rooms considered as individual units.

If, for example, the requirement for science lecture rooms as existing for an 'average' university is compared with the requirement at other utilisation levels, the differences in terms of relative capital costs can be obtained from a summation of the costs for each group of lecture rooms at the different levels.

The groups of rooms established earlier (see Chapter 4, Section c) gave the nominal sizes required for such an 'average' situation. To provide details of rooms in order to make a comparison costing, values needed to be selected from the computer tables to approximate to these nominal sizes. From this selection a series of models for lecture-room groupings was constructed in diagrammatic form (Figs. 37a–e).

These models were based on the ideas already put forward for medium size lecture blocks or 'nodes' seen as single level organisations related to the main circulation ways of science teaching areas. They aimed to provide outline designs corresponding to each of the utilisation levels while at the same time allowing for future flexibility and change.

1. It must be emphasised that the costs form a basis for comparison studies and the many possible additional items that could be required do not, for these purposes, add any extra information. As a result it is not valid to take any one total rate or price and necessarily assume that a satisfactory lecture room can be achieved within that level.

From the models the following programme of room sizes was compiled:

Utilisation factor at (h per week)	Lecture-room sizes						
10	1 at 312	1 at 260	1 at 231	1 at 208	1 at 156	2 at 117	4 at 81
					1 at 168	1 at 110	—
13†	1 at 312	1 at 260	*	1 at 208	1 at 168	2 at 117	4 at 81
15	1 at 312	1 at 260	*	1 at 209	1 at 154	2 at 110	2 at 88
20	1 at 312	1 at 260	*	*	*‡	2 at 110	2 at 88
25	1 at 312	*	*	1 at 208	*	1 at 117	2 at 81
30	1 at 312	*	*	1 at 208	*	1 at 117	1 at 81

† Existing level from the U.K. survey.

‡ A room at 160 has been omitted from all groupings to represent non-withdrawn lecture space in specific laboratory areas.

The build-up of gross floor space was produced from the same standards as for the individual rooms given earlier (only using different graph interpolation values where room sizes vary). In addition provision was made for W.C.s/cloakrooms which for individual rooms were assumed to be already provided for in the related teaching buildings (see Appendix 2 B). Other figures were taken from measurement of the design models. The resultant areas were:

Lecture groupings: Gross internal floor area						
Total Places	2,003	1,506	1,331	968	799	718
Utilisation (h)	10	13	15	20	25	30
Total F.S.	36,827	27,300	24,154	17,577	14,487	12,725
F.S./place	18·4	18·1	18·1	18·2	18·1	17·7

Each block of lecture rooms was then costed by the Quantity Surveyors to give a build-up of total capital cost and overall price per ft super. The same rates and standards for this costing were applied as in the case of the individual rooms together with an identical elemental breakdown (see Appendix 2 D). Again it must be noted that the resultant prices provide a basic level for comparison studies to be made and not a final price for which it would be possible to build lecture blocks, e.g. following items not included:

No demonstration services, fixed bench
No special rooms, e.g. projection
No lifts, extra stairs
No mechanical cooling for summer use

In particular the studies relate to a single level organisation of rooms and further research would be required to establish cost levels for different multi-storey forms.

The result of this costing of the designs for the lecture groupings showed:

Cost analysis: Lecture groupings						
Total Places	2,003	1,506	1,331	968	799	718
Utilisation (h)	10	13	15	20	25	30
Total Capital Cost £	249,800	184,000	160,500	117,600	98,100	86,900
Cost per F.S. *s.*	135·66	134·76	132·90	133·85	135·38	136·65
Cost per place £	124·7	122·2	120·6	121·5	122·9	121·0

If, however, for the same utilisation levels the same lecture theatres had not been organised in building blocks but provided within a science area as 'equivalent' single rooms what would their comparable cost have been? By taking the sizes of room and interpolating them for elements of cost compiled earlier for the standard range of

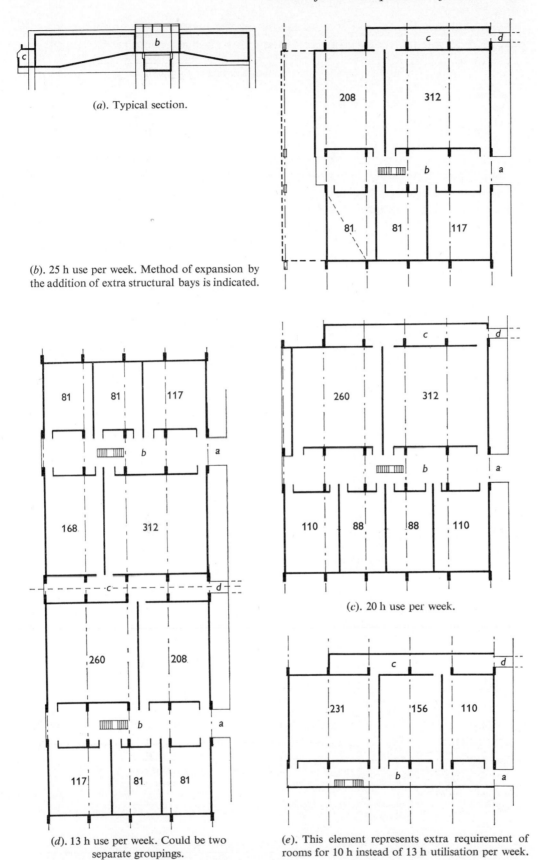

(*a*). Typical section.

(*b*). 25 h use per week. Method of expansion by the addition of extra structural bays is indicated.

(*c*). 20 h use per week.

(*d*). 13 h use per week. Could be two separate groupings.

(*e*). This element represents extra requirement of rooms for 10 h instead of 13 h utilisation per week.

Fig. 37. Models of single level lecture groupings to correspond with the science lecture-room requirements of a theoretical average English university. Different size groupings that would be needed for variations of average room utilisation in hours per week.

   a, Link to main circulation way.
   b, Foyer space with cloakrooms, plant area below.
   c, Preparation area.
   d, Link for staff and services to teaching areas below level of main circulation.

Ancillary space has been organised to approximate to 60 % of net lecture-room space.

individual theatres total room costs can be established. If these are summed up to provide 'equivalent' lecture group costs the following figures result:

Cost analysis: Individual rooms 'equivalent' to groupings						
Total Places	2,003	1,506	1,331	968	799	718
Utilisation (h)	10	13	15	20	25	30
Total Capital Cost £	290,200	220,400	186,600	136,500	113,700	97,500
Cost per F.S. *s.*	157·63	161·47	154·54	155·32	156·94	153·25
Cost per place £	144·9	146·4	140·2	141·1	142·3	135·9

A comparison between the lecture rooms required at the different levels of size/utilisation shows from these tables that the grouping of rooms into lecture blocks, as opposed to having an equivalent number of individual rooms, would provide the following savings:

Cost savings: Grouped to 'equivalent' individual rooms						
Total Places	2,003	1,506	1,331	968	799	718
Utilisation (h)	10	13	15	20	25	30
Capital cost saving, £	40,400	36,400	26,100	18,900	15,600	10,600
Capital cost saving, %	13·9	16·5	14·0	13·9	13·7	10·9
Cost per place saving, £	20·2	24·2	19·6	19·6	19·4	14·9

This table represents the differential for lecture blocks to 'equivalent' detached theatres in terms of actual building costs for a range of group sizes. From it, and from the previous tables, it is possible to make a series of comparisons on cost for individual or grouped rooms and also to interpolate readings for other groups taken from the Seat-point computer tables. The rate of change of cost for groups of rooms and for individual elements contributing to those costs can also be constructed.

What, however, appears one of the most interesting applications of these diagrams of cost is the possibility of equating efficiency of use to savings in capital cost:

The survey of existing U.K. science lecture rooms showed an average use of 13 h per week. If this utilisation were increased to 20 h per week to meet the same lecture load then the potential saving in building costs between them would be:

Utilisation	Equivalent cost (£) individual rooms	Lecture block cost (£)
a. 13 h per week	220,400	184,000
b. 20 h per week	136,500	117,600
c. Saving £	83,900	66,400
d. Saving as % of *a*	38·1	36·1

If the capital cost of building individual rooms to meet a 13 h per week utilisation is compared with the cost of a lecture block to a 20 h per week utilisation the difference is £102,800. This represents a saving of 46·7% on the cost of the individual rooms.

If the existing lecture load as above at 13 h per week were to be met by no rooms other than at 120 then from utilisation graph (see Chapter 4, Section *c*) requirement would be:

Utilisation	Rooms required	Equivalent cost (£) individual rooms
a. 13 h per week	12 at 120*	223,500
b. 20 h per week	8 at 120	149,000
c. Saving £	—	74,000
d. Saving as % of *a*	—	33·1

* From Elemental analysis of detached theatres. 120 (nom.) taken as 117 (actual).

A further comparison to this can then be made by the construction of layouts for groupings as opposed to individual rooms.

APPENDIX 1

Selected print-out from 'Seatpoint' computer program.
Values as discussed in Chapter 8 page 85

Symbols

C Horizontal centre image viewing angle, deg
P Seat width, ft
Q Row spacing, ft
V Angle from nearest eye to top of screen, deg
S Seats per row
N Number of rows
K Capacity in places

T Space front wall to front row, ft
G Gap between rear row and back of room 6W, ft
B Breadth of room, ft
L Length of room, ft
A Area LB, sq.ft
D Difference to U.G.C. space allocation, sq.ft
D/A Difference as percentage of area

SEATPOINT PROGRAM MK 3A

Image size, 5·00 ft
Room length, 6·00W
Distance image to nearest eye, 1·75W

C	P	Q	V	S	N	K	T	T+G	T+G+Q	B	L	A	D	D/A

Image size, 5·00 ft
Room length, 6·00W
Distance image to nearest eye, 2·00W

C	P	Q	V	S	N	K	T	T+G	T+G+Q	B	L	A	D	D/A

Image size, 5·00 ft
Room length, 6·00W
Distance image to nearest eye, 2·25W

C	P	Q	V	S	N	K	T	T+G	T+G+Q	B	L	A	D	D/A
45	2·00	2·75	32	11	7	77	8·50	10·75	13·50	30·00 × 30·00	900	60	6·67
50	2·00	2·75	32	13	7	91	8·50	10·75	13·50	34·00 × 30·00	1,020	80	7·84
55	2·00	2·75	32	16	7	112	8·50	10·75	13·50	40·00 × 30·00	1,200	110	9·17
60	2·00	2·75	32	19	7	133	8·50	10·75	13·50	46·00 × 30·00	1,380	140	10·14

Image size, 5·50 ft
Room length, 6·00W
Distance image to nearest eye, 1·75W

C	P	Q	V	S	N	K	T	T+G	T+G+Q	B	L	A	D	D/A

Image size, 5·50 ft
Room length, 6·00W
Distance image to nearest eye, 2·00W

C	P	Q	V	S	N	K	T	T+G	T+G+Q	B	L	A	D	D/A

Image size, 5·50 ft
Room length, 6·00W
Distance image to nearest eye, 2·25W

C	P	Q	V	S	N	K	T	T+G	T+G+Q	B	L	A	D	D/A
40	2·00	2·75	33	10	8	80	9·63	11·00	13·75	28·00 × 33·00	924	66	7·14
45	2·00	2·75	33	12	8	96	9·63	11·00	13·75	32·00 × 33·00	1,056	94	8·90
50	2·00	2·75	33	14	8	112	9·63	11·00	13·75	36·00 × 33·00	1,188	122	10·27
55	2·00	2·75	33	17	8	136	9·63	11·00	13·75	42·00 × 33·00	1,386	164	11·83
60	2·00	2·75	33	21	8	168	9·63	11·00	13·75	50·00 × 33·00	1,650	220	13·33

Image size, 6·00 ft
Room length, 6·00W
Distance image to nearest eye, 1·75W

C	P	Q	V	S	N	K	T	T+G	T+G+Q	B	L	A	D	D/A

Image size, 6·00 ft
Room length, 6·00W
Distance image to nearest eye, 2·00W

C	P	Q	V	S	N	K	T	T+G	T+G+Q	B	L	A	D	D/A
35	2·00	2·75	34	8	9	72	9·25	11·25	14·00	24·00 × 36·00	864	46	5·32
40	2·00	2·75	34	10	9	90	9·25	11·25	14·00	28·00 × 36·00	1,008	82	8·13
45	2·00	2·75	34	12	9	108	9·25	11·25	14·00	32·00 × 36·00	1,152	118	10·24
50	2·00	2·75	34	14	9	126	9·25	11·25	14·00	36·00 × 36·00	1,296	154	11·88
55	2·00	2·75	34	17	9	153	9·25	11·25	14·00	42·00 × 36·00	1,512	208	13·76
60	2·00	2·75	34	20	9	180	9·25	11·25	14·00	48·00 × 36·00	1,728	262	15·16

Image size, 6·00 ft
Room length, 6·00W
Distance image to nearest eye, 2·25W

C	P	Q	V	S	N	K	T	T+G	T+G+Q	B	L	A	D	D/A
35	2·00	2·75	34	9	9	81	10·75	11·25	14·00	26·00 × 36·00	936	64	6·84
40	2·00	2·75	34	11	9	99	10·75	11·25	14·00	30·00 × 36·00	1,080	100	9·26
45	2·00	2·75	34	13	9	117	10·75	11·25	14·00	34·00 × 36·00	1,224	136	11·11
50	2·00	2·75	34	16	9	144	10·75	11·25	14·00	40·00 × 36·00	1,440	190	13·19
55	2·00	2·75	34	19	9	171	10·75	11·25	14·00	46·00 × 36·00	1,656	244	14·73
60	2·00	2·75	34	23	9	207	10·75	11·25	14·00	54·00 × 36·00	1,944	316	16·26

Image Size, 6·50 ft
Room length, 6·00W
Distance image to nearest eye, 1·75W

C	P	Q	V	S	N	K	T	T+G	T+G+Q	B	L	A	D	D/A

Image size, 6·50 ft
Room length, 6·00W
Distance image to nearest eye, 2·00W

C	P	Q	V	S	N	K	T	T+G	T+G+Q	B	L	A	D	D/A
35	2·00	2·75	35	9	10	90	10·25	11·50	14·25	26·00 × 39·00	1,014	76	7·50
40	2·00	2·75	35	10	10	100	10·25	11·50	14·25	28·00 × 39·00	1,092	98	8·97
45	2·00	2·75	35	13	10	130	10·25	11·50	14·25	34·00 × 39·00	1,326	164	12·37
50	2·00	2·75	35	15	10	150	10·25	11·50	14·25	38·00 × 39·00	1,482	208	14·04
55	2·00	2·75	35	18	10	180	10·25	11·50	14·25	44·00 × 39·00	1,716	274	15·97
60	2·00	2·75	35	22	10	220	10·25	11·50	14·25	52·00 × 39·00	2,028	362	17·85

Image size, 6·50 ft
Room length, 6·00W
Distance image to nearest eye, 2·25W

C	P	Q	V	S	N	K	T	T+G	T+G+Q	B	L	A	D	D/A
40	2·00	2·75	30	12	9	108	11·88	14·25	17·00	32·00 × 39·00	1,248	22	1·76
45	2·00	2·75	30	14	9	126	11·88	14·25	17·00	36·00 × 39·00	1,404	46	3·28
50	2·00	2·75	30	17	9	153	11·88	14·25	17·00	42·00 × 39·00	1,638	82	5·01
55	2·00	2·75	30	20	9	180	11·88	14·25	17·00	48·00 × 39·00	1,872	118	6·30
60	2·00	2·75	30	25	9	225	11·88	14·25	17·00	58·00 × 39·00	2,262	178	7·87

Image size, 7·00 ft
Room length, 6·00W
Distance image to nearest eye, 1·75W

C	P	Q	V	S	N	K	T	T+G	T+G+Q	B	L	A	D	D/A
35	2·00	2·75	35	8	11	88	9·50	11·75	14·50	24·00 × 42·00	1,008	62	6·15
40	2·00	2·75	35	10	11	110	9·50	11·75	14·50	28·00 × 42·00	1,176	114	9·69
45	2·00	2·75	35	12	11	132	9·50	11·75	14·50	32·00 × 42·00	1,344	166	12·35
50	2·00	2·75	35	14	11	154	9·50	11·75	14·50	36·00 × 42·00	1,512	218	14·42
55	2·00	2·75	35	17	11	187	9·50	11·75	14·50	42·00 × 42·00	1,764	296	16·78
60	2·00	2·75	35	21	11	231	9·50	11·75	14·50	50·00 × 42·00	2,100	400	19·05

Image size, 7·00 ft
Room length, 6·00W
Distance image to nearest eye, 2·00W

C	P	Q	V	S	N	K	T	T+G	T+G+Q	B	L	A	D	D/A
35	2·00	2·75	35	9	11	99	11·25	11·75	14·50	26·00 × 42·00	1,092	88	8·06
40	2·00	2·75	35	11	11	121	11·25	11·75	14·50	30·00 × 42·00	1,260	140	11·11
45	2·00	2·75	35	14	11	154	11·25	11·75	14·50	36·00 × 42·00	1,512	218	14·42
50	2·00	2·75	35	16	11	176	11·25	11·75	14·50	40·00 × 42·00	1,680	270	16·07
55	2·00	2·75	35	19	11	209	11·25	11·75	14·50	46·00 × 42·00	1,932	348	18·01
60	2·00	2·75	35	24	11	264	11·25	11·75	14·50	56·00 × 42·00	2,352	478	20·32

Image size, 7·00 ft
Room length, 6·00W
Distance image to nearest eye, 2·25W

C	P	Q	V	S	N	K	T	T+G	T+G+Q	B	L	A	D	D/A
35	2·00	2·75	31	11	10	110	13·00	14·50	17·25	30·00×42·00	1,260	30	2·38
40	2·00	2·75	31	13	10	130	13·00	14·50	17·25	34·00×42·00	1,428	62	4·34
45	2·00	2·75	31	15	10	150	13·00	14·50	17·25	38·00×42·00	1,596	94	5·89
50	2·00	2·75	31	18	10	180	13·00	14·50	17·25	44·00×42·00	1,848	142	7·68
55	2·00	2·75	31	22	10	220	13·00	14·50	17·25	52·00×42·00	2,184	206	9·43
60	2·00	2·75	31	27	10	270	13·00	14·50	17·25	62·00×42·00	2,604	286	10·98

Image size, 7·50 ft
Room length, 6·00W
Distance image to nearest eye, 1·75W

C	P	Q	V	S	N	K	T	T+G	T+G+Q	B	L	A	D	D/A
35	2·00	2·75	36	9	12	108	10·38	12·00	14·75	26·00×45·00	1,170	100	8·55
40	2·00	2·75	36	11	12	132	10·38	12·00	14·75	30·00×45·00	1,350	160	11·85
45	2·00	2·75	36	13	12	156	10·38	12·00	14·75	34·00×45·00	1,530	220	14·38
50	2·00	2·75	36	15	12	180	10·38	12·00	14·75	38·00×45·00	1,710	280	16·37
55	2·00	2·75	36	18	12	216	10·38	12·00	14·75	44·00×45·00	1,980	370	18·69
60	2·00	2·75	36	22	12	264	10·38	12·00	14·75	52·00×45·00	2,340	490	20·94

Image size, 7·50 ft
Room length, 6·00W
Distance image to nearest eye, 2·00W

C	P	Q	V	S	N	K	T	T+G	T+G+Q	B	L	A	D	D/A
35	2·00	2·75	32	10	11	110	12·25	14·75	17·50	28·00×45·00	1,260	30	2·38
40	2·00	2·75	32	12	11	132	12·25	14·75	17·50	32·00×45·00	1,440	70	4·86
45	2·00	2·75	32	15	11	165	12·25	14·75	17·50	38·00×45·00	1,710	130	7·60
50	2·00	2·75	32	17	11	187	12·25	14·75	17·50	42·00×45·00	1,890	170	8·99
55	2·00	2·75	32	21	11	231	12·25	14·75	17·50	50·00×45·00	2,250	250	11·11
60	2·00	2·75	32	25	11	275	12·25	14·75	17·50	58·00×45·00	2,610	330	12·64

Image size, 7·50 ft
Room length, 6·00W
Distance image to nearest eye, 2·25W

C	P	Q	V	S	N	K	T	T+G	T+G+Q	B	L	A	D	D/A
35	2·00	2·75	32	11	11	121	14·13	14·75	17·50	30·00×45·00	1,350	50	3·70
40	2·00	2·75	32	14	11	154	14·13	14·75	17·50	36·00×45·00	1,620	110	6·79
45	2·00	2·75	32	16	11	176	14·13	14·75	17·50	40·00×45·00	1,800	150	8·33
50	2·00	2·75	32	20	11	220	14·13	14·75	17·50	48·00×45·00	2,160	230	10·65
55	2·00	2·75	32	24	11	264	14·13	14·75	17·50	56·00×45·00	2,520	310	12·30
60	2·00	2·75	32	29	11	319	14·13	14·75	17·50	66·00×45·00	2,970	410	13·80

Image size, 8·00 ft
Room length, 6·00W
Distance image to nearest eye, 1·75W

C	P	Q	V	S	N	K	T	T+G	T+G+Q	B	L	A	D	D/A

Image size, 8·00 ft
Room length, 6·00W
Distance image to nearest eye, 2·00W

C	P	Q	V	S	N	K	T	T+G	T+G+Q	B	L	A	D	D/A
35	2·00	2·75	33	11	12	132	13·25	15·00	17·75	30·00×48·00	1,440	70	4·86
40	2·00	2·75	33	13	12	156	13·25	15·00	17·75	34·00×48·00	1,632	118	7·23
45	2·00	2·75	33	16	12	192	13·25	15·00	17·75	40·00×48·00	1,920	190	9·90
50	2·00	2·75	33	19	12	228	13·25	15·00	17·75	46·00×48·00	2,208	262	11·87
55	2·00	2·75	33	22	12	264	13·25	15·00	17·75	52·00×48·00	2,496	334	13·38
60	2·00	2·75	33	27	12	324	13·25	15·00	17·75	62·00×48·00	2,976	454	15·26

Image size, 8·00 ft
Room length, 6·00W
Distance image to nearest eye, 2·25W

C	P	Q	V	S	N	K	T	T+G	T+G+Q	B	L	A	D	D/A
40	2·00	2·75	29	15	11	165	15·25	17·75	20·50	38·00×48·00	1,824	16	0·88
45	2·00	2·75	29	18	11	198	15·25	17·75	20·50	44·00×48·00	2,112	58	2·75
50	2·00	2·75	29	21	11	231	15·25	17·75	20·50	50·00×48·00	2,400	100	4·17
55	2·00	2·784	29	25	11	275	15·25	17·75	20·50	58·00×48·00	2,784	156	5·60

Image size, 8·50 ft
Room length, 6·00W
Distance image to nearest eye, 1·75W

C	P	Q	V	S	N	K	T	T+G	T+G+Q	B	L	A	D	D/A

Image size, 8·50 ft
Room length, 6·00W
Distance image to nearest eye, 2·00W

C	P	Q	V	S	N	K	T	T+G	T+G+Q	B	L	A	D	D/A
35	2·00	2·75	33	11	13	143	14·25	15·25	18·00	30·00×51·00	1,530	90	5·88
40	2·00	2·75	33	14	13	182	14·25	15·25	18·00	36·00×51·00	1,836	174	9·48
45	2·00	2·75	33	17	13	221	14·25	15·25	18·00	42·00×51·00	2,142	258	12·04
50	2·00	2·75	33	20	13	260	14·25	15·25	18·00	48·00×51·00	2,448	342	13·97
55	2·00	2·75	33	24	13	312	14·25	15·25	18·00	56·00×51·00	2,856	454	15·90

Image size, 8·50 ft
Room length, 6·00W
Distance image to nearest eye, 2·25W

C	P	Q	V	S	N	K	T	T+G	T+G+Q	B	L	A	D	D/A
35	2·00	2·75	30	13	12	156	16·38	18·00	20·75	34·00×51·00	1,734	16	0·92
40	2·00	2·75	30	16	12	192	16·38	18·00	20·75	40·00×51·00	2,040	70	3·43
45	2·00	2·75	30	19	12	228	16·38	18·00	20·75	46·00×51·00	2,346	124	5·29
50	2·00	2·75	30	22	12	264	16·38	18·00	20·75	52·00×51·00	2,652	178	6·71
55	2·00	2·75	30	27	12	324	16·38	18·00	20·75	62·00×51·00	3,162	268	8·48

Image size, 9·00 ft
Room length, 6·00W
Distance image to nearest eye, 1·75W

C	P	Q	V	S	N	K	T	T+G	T+G+Q	B	L	A	D	D/A
35	2·00	2·75	34	11	14	154	13·00	15·50	18·25	30·00×54·00	1,620	110	6·79
40	2·00	2·75	34	13	14	182	13·00	15·50	18·25	34·00×54·00	1,836	174	9·48
45	2·00	2·75	34	15	14	210	13·00	15·50	18·25	38·00×54·00	2,052	238	11·60
50	2·00	2·75	34	18	14	252	13·00	15·50	18·25	44·00×54·00	2,376	334	14·06
55	2·00	2·75	34	22	14	308	13·00	15·50	18·25	52·00×54·00	2,808	462	16·45

Image size, 9·00 ft
Room length, 6·00W
Distance image to nearest eye, 2·00W

C	P	Q	V	S	N	K	T	T+G	T+G+Q	B	L	A	D	D/A
35	2·00	2·75	34	12	14	168	15·25	15·50	18·25	32·00×54·00	1,728	142	8·22
40	2·00	2·75	34	15	14	210	15·25	15·50	18·25	38·00×54·00	2,052	238	11·60
45	2·00	2·75	34	18	14	252	15·25	15·50	18·25	44·00×54·00	2,376	334	14·06
50	2·00	2·75	34	21	14	294	15·25	15·50	18·25	50·00×54·00	2,700	430	15·93

Image size, 9·00 ft
Room length, 6·00W
Distance image to nearest eye, 2·25W

C	P	Q	V	S	N	K	T	T+G	T+G+Q	B	L	A	D	D/A
35	2·00	2·75	30	14	13	182	17·50	18·25	21·00	36·00×54·00	1,944	66	3·40
40	2·00	2·75	30	16	13	208	17·50	18·25	21·00	40·00×54·00	2,160	110	5·09
45	2·00	2·75	30	20	13	260	17·50	18·25	21·00	48·00×54·00	2,592	198	7·64
50	2·00	2·75	30	24	13	312	17·50	18·25	21·00	56·00×54·00	3,024	286	9·46

Image size, 9·50 ft
Room length, 6·00W
Distance image to nearest eye, 1·75W

C	P	Q	V	S	N	K	T	T+G	T+G+Q	B	L	A	D	D/A
35	2·00	2·75	35	11	15	165	13·88	15·75	18·50	30·00×57·00	1,710	130	7·60
40	2·00	2·75	35	13	15	195	13·88	15·75	18·50	34·00×57·00	1,938	202	10·42
45	2·00	2·75	35	16	15	240	13·88	15·75	18·50	40·00×57·00	2,280	310	13·60
50	2·00	2·75	35	19	15	285	13·88	15·75	18·50	46·00×57·00	2,622	418	15·94

Image size, 9·50 ft
Room length, 6·00W
Distance image to nearest eye, 2·00W

C	P	Q	V	S	N	K	T	T+G	T+G+Q	B	L	A	D	D/A
35	2·00	2·75	31	13	14	182	16·25	18·50	21·25	34·00 × 57·00	1,938	72	3·72
40	2·00	2·75	31	15	14	210	16·25	18·50	21·25	38·00 × 57·00	2,166	124	5·72
45	2·00	2·75	31	19	14	266	16·25	18·50	21·25	46·00 × 57·00	2,622	228	8·70
50	2·00	2·75	31	22	14	308	16·25	18·50	21·25	52·00 × 57·00	2,964	306	10·32

Image size, 9·50 ft
Room length, 6·00W
Distance image to nearest eye, 2·25W

C	P	Q	V	S	N	K	T	T+G	T+G+Q	B	L	A	D	D/A
40	2·00	2·75	28	17	13	221	18·63	21·25	24·00	42·00 × 57·00	2,394	6	0·25
45	2·00	2·75	28	21	13	273	18·63	21·25	24·00	50·00 × 57·00	2,850	70	2·46
50	2·00	2·75	28	25	13	325	18·63	21·25	24·00	58·00 × 57·00	3,306	134	4·05

Image size, 10·00 ft
Room length, 6·00W
Distance image to nearest eye, 1·75W

C	P	Q	V	S	N	K	T	T+G	T+G+Q	B	L	A	D	D/A
35	2·00	2·75	35	12	16	192	14·75	16·00	18·75	32·00 × 60·00	1,920	190	9·90
40	2·00	2·75	35	14	16	224	14·75	16·00	18·75	36·00 × 60·00	2,160	270	12·50
45	2·00	2·75	35	17	16	272	14·75	16·00	18·75	42·00 × 60·00	2,520	390	15·48
50	2·00	2·75	35	20	16	320	14·75	16·00	18·75	48·00 × 60·00	2,880	510	17·71

Image size, 10·00 ft
Room length, 6·00W
Distance image to nearest eye, 2·00W

C	P	Q	V	S	N	K	T	T+G	T+G+Q	B	L	A	D	D/A
35	2·00	2·75	32	14	15	210	17·25	18·75	21·50	36·00 × 60·00	2,160	130	6·02
40	2·00	2·75	32	16	15	240	17·25	18·75	21·50	40·00 × 60·00	2,400	190	7·92
45	2·00	2·75	32	20	15	300	17·75	18·75	21·50	48·00 × 60·00	2,880	310	10·76

Image size, 10·00 ft
Room length, 6·00W
Distance image to nearest eye, 2·25W

C	P	Q	V	S	N	K	T	T+G	T+G+Q	B	L	A	D	D/A

The computer used by Messrs Monk and Dunstone to run this program was a National-Elliott 803 having a 8,192 39-bit word core store and an automatic floating point unit.

The program and data were read into the computer using 5-channel paper tape and the results were punched out of the computer on to paper tape. This was then fed to a Friden Flexowriter—an automatic typewriter with a 16 in. wide carriage—which printed the results on to paper.

The program was written in Elliott Autocode and could be run on any 803 installation with an automatic floating point unit and paper tape facilities.

APPENDIX 2

Analysis for comparative costing

A. *Individual lecture rooms—build up of gross internal floor area*

Room size	77		117		165		192		240		272		320	
	Total FS	FS per seat	Total FS	FS per seat	Total FS	FS per seat	Total FS	FS per seat	Total FS	FS per seat	Total FS	FS per seat	Total FS	FS per seat
Lecture theatre	900	11·7	1,224	10·4	1,710	10·4	1,920	10·0	2,280	9·5	2,520	9·2	2,880	9·0
Foyer	425	5·5	468	4·0	513	3·1	577	3·0	720	3·0	819	3·0	960	3·0
Prep. room	—	—	—	—	165	1·0	193	1·0	240	1·0	273	1·0	320	1·0
Plant room	300	3·9	340	2·9	380	2·3	400	2·1	400	1·7	588	2·2	672	2·1
W.C.s	—	—	—	—	—	—	—	—	—	—	—	—	—	—
Tanks	150	1·9	150	1·3	150	0·9	150	0·8	150	0·6	150	0·5	150	0·4
Wall thickness	30	0·4	34	0·3	58	0·3	66	0·3	66	0·3	70	0·3	80	0·3
Other	—	—	—	—	—	—	—	—	—	—	—	—	—	—
	1,805	23·4	2,216	18·9	2,976	18·0	3,306	17·2	3,856	16·1	4,420	16·2	5,062	15·8

B. *Lecture groupings—build up of gross internal floor area*

Total places	2,003		1,506		1,331		968		799		718	
Equivalent utilisation hours per week	10		13		15		20		25		30	
	Total FS	FS per seat	Total FS	FS per seat	Total FS	FS per seat	Total FS	FS per seat	Total FS	FS per seat	Total FS	FS per seat
Lecture theatre	21,384	10·7	15,660	10·4	13,636	10·2	10,368	10·7	8,460	10·6	7,202	10·1
Foyer	6,062	3·0	4,568	3·0	3,985	3·0	2,898	3·0	2,397	3·0	2,162	3·0
Prep. room	1,428	0·7	935	0·6	935	0·7	572	0·6	520	0·7	520	0·7
Plant room	1,960	0·9	1,680	1·1	1,464	1·1	1,162	1·2	1,120	1·4	1,150	1·6
W.C.s	4,101	2·1	2,887	1·9	2,521	1·9	1,736	1·8	1,277	1·5	1,012	1·4
Tank room	1,175	0·6	1,050	0·7	662	0·5	537	0·6	460	0·6	460	0·6
Wall thickness	717	0·4	520	0·4	478	0·35	304	0·3	253	0·3	219	0·3
Other	—	—	—	—	473	0·35	—	—	—	—	—	—
	36,827	18·4	27,300	18·1	24,154	18·1	17,577	18·2	14,487	18·1	12,725	17·7

c. *Elemental analysis of individual lecture rooms*

Room size	77		117		165		192		240		272		320	
	s. per FS	Total £	s. per FS	Total £	s. per FS	Total £	s. per FS	Total £	s. per FS	Total £	s. per FS	Total £	s. per FS	Total £
Foundations	9·97	900	10·59	1,173	11·36	1,691	11·41	1,885	11·46	2,210	11·57	2,557	11·57	2,928
Frame	11·79	1,064	10·04	1,112	7·80	1,160	7·16	1,184	6·64	1,280	5·79	1,280	5·06	1,280
Upper floors	10·55	952	10·62	1,177	10·06	1,497	10·31	1,703	11·03	2,127	11·10	2,454	11·09	2,808
Roof	15·11	1,364	15·31	1,696	15·26	2,270	15·59	2,577	15·79	3,046	15·30	3,381	15·03	3,803
Stairs	4·99	450	4·06	450	3·02	450	2·72	450	2·33	450	2·04	450	1·78	450
External walls	26·35	2,378	24·50	2,715	23·03	3,427	22·02	2,638	21·55	4,155	20·19	4,463	18·29	4,628
Windows and external doors	3·48	314	3·09	342	2·45	365	2·38	393	2·04	393	1·91	421	1·66	421
Internal walls and partitions	4·19	377	3·99	442	3·95	583	3·93	650	3·67	708	3·51	775	3·34	846
Internal doors	1·44	130	1·17	130	1·04	155	0·94	155	0·80	155	0·70	155	0·61	155
Wall finishes	9·66	372	9·31	1,032	8·62	1,282	8·38	1,385	8·29	1,599	7·71	1,704	7·19	1,821
Floor finishes	7·01	633	7·30	809	7·29	1,085	7·71	1,274	7·59	1,464	7·48	1,653	7·54	1,908
Ceiling finishes	10·38	936	10·77	1,193	10·61	1,579	10·72	1,773	11·04	2,129	10·73	2,372	10·78	2,729
Fittings	0·66	60	0·54	60	1·08	160	0·97	160	0·83	160	0·73	160	0·63	160
Sanitary fittings and plumbing	0·55	50	0·45	50	0·47	70	0·43	70	0·34	70	0·32	70	0·28	70
Mechanical services	27·11	2,447	23·23	2,574	20·71	3,082	22·25	3,676	19·96	3,849	18·28	4,040	16·39	4,149
Electrical services	17·17	1,550	17·84	1,977	18·08	2,689	18·15	2,999	18·32	3,529	18·05	3,990	18·04	4,566
Preliminaries	16·04	1,448	15·28	1,693	14·48	2,155	14·51	2,397	14·17	2,732	13·54	2,992	12·93	3,272
	176·45	15,925	168·09	18,625	159·31	23,706	159·58	26,369	155·85	30,056	148·95	32,917	142·21	35,994
Cost place, £	206·8		159·2		143·7		137·3		125·2		121·00		112·5	

D. *Cost comparison—lecture groupings to 'equivalent' range of individual rooms*

Total places	2,003		1,506		1,331		968		799		718	
Equivalent utilisation hours per week	10		13		15		20		25		30	
	Group £000	Equiv. £000	Group £000	Equiv. £000	Group £000	Equiv. £000	Group £000	Equiv. £000	Group £000	Equiv. £000	Group £000	Equiv. £000
Foundations	22·2	19·9	16·3	15·0	14·6	13·0	10·6	9·4	8·7	7·9	7·6	6·9
Frame	10·4	14·9	8·0	11·4	6·8	9·3	4·8	6·9	4·0	5·7	3·6	4·7
Upper floors	19·1	19·3	14·1	14·7	12·6	12·6	9·3	9·4	7·5	7·7	6·6	6·7
Roof	24·8	27·8	18·2	21·0	16·4	18·1	11·9	13·2	9·7	11·0	8·5	9·6
Stairs	1·4	5·8	0·9	4·5	0·9	3·6	0·5	2·7	0·5	2·3	0·5	1·8
External walls	14·9	41·2	11·7	31·2	10·0	26·3	8·2	19·2	7·5	15·9	7·4	13·5
Windows and doors	1·6	4·6	1·4	3·5	1·0	2·9	0·8	2·1	0·7	1·8	0·7	1·5
Walls and partitions	14·1	7·0	9·4	5·3	7·3	4·5	4·7	3·2	4·0	2·7	3·4	2·3
Internal doors	2·1	1·8	1·4	1·4	1·2	1·1	0·7	0·8	0·5	0·7	0·5	0·6
Wall finishes	15·8	15·4	11·3	11·7	9·7	9·8	7·0	7·2	5·9	5·9	5·1	5·0
Floor finishes	14·6	13·3	10·7	10·0	9·3	8·7	6·9	6·4	5·6	5·2	4·9	4·6
Ceiling finishes	19·7	19·4	14·5	14·7	12·8	12·6	9·5	9·2	7·9	7·7	6·7	6·7
Fittings	1·1	1·3	0·6	1·0	0·3	0·8	0·3	0·6	0·2	0·5	0·2	0·4
Sanitary fittings and plumbing	1·7	0·7	1·3	0·6	1·0	0·5	0·6	0·3	0·6	0·3	0·6	0·3
Mechanical services	31·1	39·0	23·6	29·9	21·0	24·7	15·5	18·1	13·1	15·3	11·7	12·8
Electrical installation	33·4	32·4	24·6	24·5	21·7	21·1	16·1	15·4	13·2	12·8	11·4	11·2
Preliminaries	21·8	26·4	16·0	20·0	13·9	17·0	10·2	12·4	8·5	10·3	7·5	8·9
	249·8	290·2	184·0	220·4	160·5	186·6	117·6	136·5	98·1	113·7	86·9	97·5
Cost differential £000	40·4		36·4		26·1		18·9		15·6		10·6	

This build up of elements and prices was prepared by Messrs Monk and Dunstone, Quantity Surveyors, with the assistance of Messrs Edward A. Pearce and Partners, Consulting Engineers.

BIBLIOGRAPHY

The academic context to the lecture room

1 *The Idea of a University*, by J. H. Newman (ed. 1947). Longmans Green and Co.
2 *The Art of Lecturing*, by G. Kitson Clark and W. Bidder Clark. Cambridge: Heffer.
3 *Report of the Committee on Higher Education* (chairman Robbins). H.M.S.O. 1963.
4 Architecture and the Sociology of University Life, by M. Cassidy in *Universities Quarterly*, September 1964.
5 *Report of Committee on University Teaching Methods* (chairman Hale). U.G.C. H.M.S.O. 1964.
6 *A University in the Making*, by A. E. Sloman. B.B.C. 1964.
7 *The Essence of Higher Education*, by P. Marris. Routledge and Kegan Paul, 1964.
8 *The Two Biologies*, by J. W. S. Pringle. O.U.P. 1963.
9 *New Media in Higher Education*, by J. Brown and W. Thornton. Association Education, 1963.
10 *Audio-Visual Aids in Higher Scientific Education*. U.G.C. H.M.S.O. 1965.
11 *Lecture Experiments in Chemistry*, by G. Fowles (6th ed.), London: Bell, 1963.
12 Physics: Laboratory Teaching, by R. G. Chambers, in *Bulletin Institute of Physics*, April 1964.
13 Design for Mechanical Learning. *Architectural Record*, May 1964.
14 Teaching Machines for Schools. *Architectural Forum*, August 1963.
15 *Programmed Instruction*, by W. Schramm. Fund for Advancement of Education, 1962.
16 *Closed Circuit Television in Education in Great Britain*. National Committee for Audio Visual Aids, 1965.

The architectural context to the lecture room

17 *Memoirs of the Life and Works of Sir Christopher Wren*, by James Elmes. London, 1823.
18 *Dictionary of Architecture*, vol. v. Architectural Publication Society, London, 1869.
19 Clarendon Laboratory, Oxford. *Builder*, 8 May 1869.
20 Owens College, Manchester. *Builder*, 4 February 1871.
21 University of Basle: Auditoria Building. *Architectural Review*, August 1945.
22 University of Saarbrucken, Lecture Complex. *Bauen and Wohnen*, no. 11, 1952.
23 Tokio, Meiji University, Lecture Theatres. *Kenchiku Bunka*, no. 102, 1955.
24 C.U.S.A. Extension. *Architectural Design*, October 1959.
25 Sidgwick Avenue Cambridge. Lecture Rooms. *Architectural Review*, February 1960.
26 Oxford Museum. Lecture Room. *Architectural Review*, December 1961.
27 Edinburgh University. Eng. Lecture Theatre: Cost Analysis. *Architect's Journal*, 9 March 1961.
28 Hamburg University. Auditorium Building. *Architectural Review*, March 1961.
29 Wolfson Institute, Hammersmith. *Architectural Design*, August 1961.
30 T.H. Stuttgart. Lecture Room Building. *Werk*, April 1962.
31 Manchester College of Science and Technology. Lecture Block. *Architectural Review*, October 1962.
32 Institute of Technology, Delft. Lecture Block. *Bauen and Wohnen*, 1963.
33 Leicester University. Department of Engineering. *Architectural Design*, February 1964.
34 University of Manchester; Roscoe Building. *Architect's Journal*, 22 January 1964.
35 State University of Technology, Santiago. Divisible Hall. *Architectural Design*, April 1964.
36 Hull University. Department of Physics. *Architect's Journal*, 21 April 1965.

University planning

37 Universities. Historical. *Architectural Review*, October 1957.
38 Universities Number. *Architectural Review*, October 1963.
39 Campus Planning in California. *Architectural Forum*, March 1963.
40 Universities Number. *L'Architecture d'Aujourdhui*, April 1963.
41 Universities Number. *Bauen and Wohnen*, August 1964.
42 New U.S. Campuses. *Architectural Record*, November 1964.
43 University Development 1957–62. H.M.S.O. 1964.
44 Returns for Universities and University Colleges 1963–64. U.G.C. H.M.S.O. 1965.
45 Berlin University Project. *Architectural Design*, August 1964.
46 New Thinking for New Universities. *Architectural Association Journal*, June 1964.
47 Flexibility for University Building, by H. G. Schenk, in *Werk*, April 1962.
48 *Bricks and Mortarboards*. Educational Facilities Laboratories, N.Y.

49 *Campus Planning*, by R. P. Dober. New York: Reinhold, 1964.
50 Science Building, by J. L. Martin, in *Architectural Design*, December 1964.
51 Long-Term Needs of Scientific Departments. *Cambridge University Reporter*, 8 December 1965.
52 University of Leeds—Development Plan, 1960, and Review, 1963.
53 University of York—Development Plan, 1962–72.
54 University of Warwick—Development Plan, 1964.
55 *Die Universität Bochum. Gesamtplanung*. Stuttgart: Karl Kramer 1965.

Utilisation and space standards

56 *A Restudy of the needs of California in Higher Education*. California State Department of Education, 1955.
57 *A Master Plan for Higher Education in California 1960–75*. California State Department of Education, 1960.
58 *Progress Report on the Study of Utilisation of Physical Facilities*. Co-ordinating Council for Higher Education, San Francisco, 1965.
59 *Determining Student Capacity in Existing Physical Facilities in California's Junior Colleges*. Co-ordinating Council for Higher Education, San Francisco, 1965.
60 Use of Plant, by B. R. Williams, in *Manchester School*, May 1963.
61 Construction of timetables, by Elizabeth D. Barraclough, in *The Computer Journal*, July 1965 (vol. 18, no. 2).
62 *Programmierung der Ruhr Universität Bochum*. Die Bauverwaltung, Dusseldorf, March 1965.
63 *Notes on Procedure: Non-recurrent Grants*. U.G.C. H.M.S.O. 1965.
64 *Empfehlungen des Wissenschaftstrates zur Aufstellung von Raumprogrammen*. Bonn, November 1963.

Design criteria for the lecture room

65 *Elements et Theorie de L'Architecture*, by J. Gaudet. Paris, 1909.
66 *Acoustics in relation to Architecture and Building*, by T. Roger Smith. Crosby Lockwood, London ed. 1895.
67 *Architectural Graphic Standards*, by C. G. Ramsey and H. R. Sleeper. New York: Wiley.
68 *Bauentwurfslehre*, by E. Neufert. Ullstein Fachverlag, 1962.
69 Planning Notes for Engineering Lecture Rooms, Monash University, by Bates, Smart and McCutcheon, in *Architecture in Australia*, December 1962.
70 Information Sheets from *Architect's Journal*:

    1185. Anthropometric data, 13 February 1963.
    1264. L.C.C. auditoria requirements, 15 July 1964.
    1274. Cinema layout and sight lines, 9 September 1964.
    1307. Teaching machines, 16 December 1964.
    1309–11. Teaching aids, 23 December 1964.
    1369. Projector Equipment, 2 February 1966.

71 *Large Hall Projectors*. E. Leitz, G.m.b.h., Wetzlar, Germany.
72 *The Overhead Projector*. Report 4 National Committee for Audio Visual Aids, London, 1965.
73 Planning of Larger Lecture Rooms; Design Study, by V. Aschoff, in *Deutshe Bauzeitshaft*, 1962, no 10.
74 Investigation into the Requirements for New Lecture Theatres. Report of the working party, University of Sussex, 1965.
75 *New Spaces for Learning*. Rensselaer Polytechnic Institute. New York, 1962.
76 *Studie uber Hörsaalplanung*, by B. Beyerle. Finanzministerium, Baden Württemberg, (?) 1964.
77 Bilder zur Geschichte der Horsale (unpublished thesis). Gerhard Warth, Heilbronn, (?) 1965.
78 Gutachtergruppe fur Hörsaalplanung Ruhr Universität Bochum; (unpublished), office Professor Fritz Eller; Aachen, 1965.
79 *Lecture Theatres and their Lighting*, Report no. 5, I.E.S. 1963.
80 *Acoustics, Noise and Buildings*, by P. H. Parkin and H. R. Humphreys. Faber, 1958.
81 *Teaching Laboratories*. Symposium R.I.B.A. 1958.
82 *Laboratory Planning*, by J. F. Munce. London: Butterworths, 1962.
83 *Laboratory Planning for Chemistry and Chemical Engineering* (ed. H. F. Lewis). New York: Reinhold, 1962.
84 *Modern Physics Buildings*, by R. Palmer and W. Rice. New York: Reinhold, 1961.

Related bibliographies

Laboratories and Lecture Rooms. Bibliography O.E.C.D. May 1962.
Assembly Halls and Auditoria (1954–63). R.I.B.A. Library.
University Buildings (1955–61). R.I.B.A. Library.
University Buildings (1961–64). R.I.B.A. Library.
University Planning. Architectural Association, 1964.

INDEX

Numbers in italic refer to illustrations; numbers with an asterisk refer to footnotes